GW00673385

Frank Bernard Halford CBE FRAeS MSAE

ROLLS-ROYCE HERITAGE TRUST

BOXKITE TO JET

– the remarkable career of Frank B Halford

Douglas R Taylor

HISTORICAL SERIES No 28

Published in 1999 by the
Rolls-Royce Heritage Trust
P O Box 31 Derby England DE24 8BJ

ISBN: 1 872922 16 3

The Historical Series is published as a joint initiative by the Rolls-Royce Heritage Trust and the Sir Henry Royce Memorial Foundation.

Previous volumes published in the Series are listed at the rear, together with volumes available in the Rolls-Royce Heritage Trust Technical Series.

Cover Picture: Major Frank B Halford, RFC/RAF 1918/19 (Ann Spring).

Books are available from:
Rolls-Royce Heritage Trust, Rolls-Royce plc, Moor Lane, PO Box 31, Derby DE24 8BJ

Origination and Reproduction by Neartone Ltd, Arnold, Nottingham
Printed by Premier Print, Glaisdale Parkway, Bilborough, Nottingham

CONTENTS

INTRODUCTION

The Historical Series of books published by the Trust aims to record the history of the products, places and people of Rolls-Royce and the companies that, over the years, have been assimilated to create the present organisation. Earlier biographies in the Series have included Hives, Rolls, Royce and Fedden, four of the giants of British aviation history. It was with great surprise and delight that out of the blue we were sent a biography of one of the great unsung heroes of our industry, Major Frank B Halford. The manuscript had been written by Douglas Taylor who joined Frank Halford's design organisation in 1936 and held a series of posts until 1951 when he moved to the oil and power industries before finally retiring as a consultant in 1986.

Douglas has held a life-long interest in vintage cars and early aviation powerplants and is a volunteer at the Brooklands Museum where much of his meticulous research is carried out. This book chronicles the life and career of Halford spanning his early flying at Brooklands, the work with Ricardo and Airdisco, designing for de Havilland and Napier and finally his work on the early jets and rockets. In telling this story, Douglas Taylor has filled an important gap in aviation history and we are privileged to bring it to a wider audience on Douglas' behalf.

Richard Haigh
Chief Executive, Rolls-Royce Heritage Trust

FOREWORD

by Mrs Patricia Draper
Frank Halford's daughter

Finally, forty years after my father's death, we now have a complete and thorough biography of his engineering career.

I cannot add or comment on any of the technical aspects of this book, but I would like to mention one or two of my father's traits which proved to be the foundation of his character and talent. Engines were his life from the moment he went away to boarding school at Felsted. In fact, one of his excellent school reports reminded my grandparents "that Frank must realise there are other subjects in the world to study outside the engine workshop", but that was always the top priority for him.

The staircase at my grandparents' home was lined with intricate engineering drawings (of subjects like water pumps) which he drafted at the age of fourteen and fifteen.

As he pursued his career, he was known for his loyalty, generosity and fairness to deserving staff no matter what their level. He was particularly charitable whenever there was a health or financial problem and I know of many draughtsmen, engineers, etc who benefited from his generosity.

I worked directly for him for a period during World War II. He was a strict taskmaster and wasted no words. I have been at meetings where an engineer, who had worked for months on a specific problem, was most anxious to describe his work in detail. My father would politely but firmly make him condense his report so that the meeting could progress.

He was fascinated by speed whether it was that of a motor cycle, racing car or aircraft. To accompany him in his car illustrated not only that fact, but also how uncanny his talent was for spatial judgement. In other words, we had what I would term some close calls.

The combination of his brilliance and his vision, combined with the above brief summary of his character, leads me to quote from the US Supreme Court Judge and philosopher, Oliver Wendell Holmes: *"A man must feel the action and fashion of his time at the price of being judged not to have lived"*. By that standard, my father had a very full life.

Finally, I would like to thank Douglas Taylor for all his hours of research and travel which were involved in the production of this truly memorable biography of my father.

Pat Draper
Marblehead, USA, March 1996
(Pat Draper died 11th September 1998)

PREFACE

The decision to chronicle the career of Frank Bernard Halford, CBE, FRAeS, MSAE, first came to mind whilst researching in the library of the Brooklands Museum. In the process of referring to the Journal of the Royal Aeronautical Society for April 1959, I found it included the publication of the first Halford Memorial Lecture, "Frank Bernard Halford 1894-1955" by John L P Brodie, then Engineering Director, the de Havilland Engine Company, and Halford's right-hand man and friend for over forty years.

In the 1930s and 1940s, I had been a junior member of Halford's design staff and reading John Brodie's paper revived memories of those fascinating days. As a detailed record of a remarkable career has not been set down, I was determined that the life and designs of an engineer of such importance to the British aviation industry should be recognised. This decision started a three-year investigative journey through the past, starting in 1840 through to 1955.

Although many technical papers expound areas of his engineering work and publications devoted to motor cycle and motor car racing have noted his involvement in their sport, his service in the Royal Flying Corps, in which he attained the rank of major (a title which he was identified in business), has been referred to in scant detail. Also his association with Sir Harry Ricardo, Sir Geoffrey de Havilland and D Napier & Son Ltd is recorded only as an appendage to accounts of those eminent men and well known companies. He ranks highly alongside his contemporary engine designers, among whom were Sir Stanley Hooker (Rolls-Royce and Bristol), A J Rowledge (Napier and Rolls-Royce), Sir Roy Fedden (Bristol), F R Smith and Harry Cantrill (Armstrong Siddeley).

Halford was probably the first to produce a car engine which was fitted with an exhaust-driven turbo-supercharger some fifty-four years before the turbo-blower was used in a production car. He created the series of aero-engines, noted for their reliability and economy, which enabled light aircraft to become popular worldwide. He designed the most powerful piston aero-engine of its day and produced the jet engine which powered the first flight, in March 1943, of the Gloster F9/40 jet plane, prototype of the Meteor, and this engine became the first production jet engine. Halford was responsible for providing the power requirements of aircraft over a forty year period, which embraced two world wars.

Of the multitude of designs, nearly sixty types of engines were actually manufactured plus many other progressive projects which existed on the drawing board but did not proceed further, due to changing markets or increasing demands for development of existing products.

His was a questing spirit and he was endowed with boundless energy, enthusiasm and a determination to see through to a satisfactory conclusion each and every enterprise in which he was engaged, be it in professional or private life, and he succeeded in filling his sixty-one years to the full.

He left Nottingham University College before completing a degree course and did not have the academic qualifications usually required as a basis for a career in engineering. Certainly, from the age of 18, his consuming interest was with the internal combustion engine and it very quickly proved that he was a 'natural' in this field. By the time he completed his RFC service and returned to civilian life, he had also acquired considerable acumen in matters of business. His future career gave proof that, in his case, the lack of a degree in engineering presented no obstacle.

Strongly independent, he retained his freedom as a consultant and it was not until his association with the Napier Company that a position of technical director was reluctantly accepted. Even so, he maintained his own flourishing consultancy, steadily building up a staff of designers and draughtsmen to handle the increasing demands of the industry and shrewdly keeping one jump ahead by designing the types of power units the aircraft manufacturers would be seeking for their next range of aircraft.

His great friend, Major G P Bulman, Director of Engine Research and Development at the Air Ministry, has said, "He was the essentially creative artist, anxious to get on with the next and a little too apt to leave to his devoted staff the drudgery and sweat of carrying his last-but-one design into production". This may well have been so, but Halford had built up a team of outstanding design engineers so that he could devote his talents to devising the engines he considered would provide the needs of the industry in the future years – and he was invariably right! He was always assessing the design of other engines and noted those areas from which he could benefit his own designs and never ceased producing ideas for his team to research.

I first met the Major when, in 1936, I was offered the most junior position in his Golden Square, London office, that of producing blueprints. Having previously spent the required time in the workshops, necessary for consideration of a draughtsman's position, my goal was to enter the drawing office and progress to design draughtsman. It was going to be a couple of years, via the drawings library, the production drawing office (updating specification sheets for issue to the RAF and civil users) and then into the stress office for a year, before I was permitted to sit at a drawing board as a junior draughtsman.

Frank Halford operated an enlightened employment policy. He would suggest that, after an appropriate number of years with him, the younger staff should leave and work for other companies to broaden their experience. As he said, "The way we do things is not the only way or necessarily the best way. Go and get experience elsewhere and come back. There will always be a place for you." This was an excellent philosophy, but it became impossible to keep in existence after 1939 because of Government restrictions imposed during the war years. After nearly eleven years, I did move on into special machine design, but as life worked out, did not return to the aircraft industry. However, the training received at Halford's provided a sound basis for a career in engineering design.

The experience of his senior designers were evident in the breadth of their engineering skills in the areas of engine design for which they were responsible. They decided the most suitable material for each part that the machining operations required could be performed by existing machines in the works and also designed any special jigs and tools that might be required.

It is my earnest hope that this book will ensure Frank Bernard Halford is remembered and recorded in his proper position in this country's aviation history.

In researching for this book, I have contacted many people and made requests of their time and efforts to provide details and verify facts. Without exception, I have received unstinting responses and can only offer my most grateful thanks and appreciation of their interest in the project.

Of the many, I must extend my particular gratitude to the librarians of the Royal Aeronautical Society, the Royal Automobile Club and the Brooklands Museum for allowing me access to their archives. Also to Dr Murray Roberts – Secretary of the Old Felstedian Society – who, in addition to providing details from the school, was instrumental in putting me in touch with a relative; to Malcolm Wright – Ricardo Consulting Engineers Ltd; to Mike Goodall of the Brooklands Museum and to John Granger for his painstaking review of the manuscript. Most of all, my most grateful thanks to Halford's daughter and step-daughter – Mrs Patricia Draper and Mrs Ann Spring, who most generously unearthed family papers and photographs for my perusal and were able to recall so many personal details.

Douglas R Taylor
West Sussex
1999

Whose youthful spirit, in me regenerate,
Doth with twofold vigor lift me up
To reach at victory above my head.

W Shakespeare
King Richard II

It is one thing to have an idea.
It is another to have the technical
*   and executive ability to give it flesh.*
It is another to have the tenacity of
*   purpose to drive through to success*
*   unshaken in confidence.*

Lord Kings Norton (1947)

Grandfather – Robert Halford
(Notts County Library)

Father – Harry Baker Halford
(Notts County Library)

Mother – Ethel Halford
(Patricia Draper)

Brother – Leslie Robert Halford From a
sketch by Stanley Parker
(Notts County Library)

12

BOXKITE TO JET

CHAPTER ONE

The Halfords

This narrative must begin in the city of Nottingham, the centre over the years of a famous lace and textile industry, and is in recognition of the outstanding contribution made to aviation by the son of a city alderman and sheriff. His name was Frank Bernard Halford.

The Halford family have been established in Nottingham for generations. Records show that the family had lived at Carter Gate in the 1740s. Robert Halford, the grandfather of Frank, was born there in 1840 and attended Dame Agnes Meller's School in Stoney Street. He was apprenticed to the lace trade but when his employer suffered severe financial problems he had to seek other employment. A job was available in the estate agency of a Mr E M Kidd and Robert Halford's career became established.

In 1865, he entered into partnership with Charles Baker, who was already well positioned in the same business, and they founded the firm of Baker and Halford in premises near Long Row. As business expanded, they moved first to Beastmarket Hill and later to St Peter's Church Walk.

Robert married and the family grew with the birth of two sons, Harry Baker in 1866 and Bernard Orme in 1870. He had a further son and four daughters. Robert was recognised as a man of sound business acumen and solid character and, in 1876, he became connected with the Nottingham & Notts Banking Company. By this time, he had been joined in the estate business by both sons and the name of the firm changed to Baker, Halford and Sons. They then occupied offices in St Peter's Gate.

In 1891, Robert was elected to the Board of the bank and was appointed Chairman. He held this position until his death. He acquired other business interests in which he held senior posts. He was Chairman of the Midland Board of the Commercial Union Insurance Co, Chairman of James Shipstone Ltd, Star Brewery at Basford. He was a member of the Institute of Bankers and the Institute of Directors and a director of the Church Cemetery Company. Appointed a magistrate in 1891, he remained on the Bench for the rest of his life.

He had a great interest in sport and was a member of the Notts County Football Club, being appointed a director on 2 June 1890 and later vice-chairman when he assisted in the formation of the club under limited liability rules. He left the Board in May 1892 whilst retaining his interest in the club's activities and sixteen years later he was appointed Club President, finally

Felsted School   (Dr A M Roberts)

Engineering workshop – Felsted School   (Dr A M Roberts)

leaving on 26 September 1910. He also held the presidency of the Notts County Cricket Club. In addition, he was president of the Notts Church Football Association, of which his eldest son, Harry, became Chairman. Robert provided a stained glass window in St Jude's Church, Nottingham, in memory of his forebears. He died on 30 September 1910 at the age of 70; the funeral being attended by many of the city's notables. Sons Harry and Bernard carried on the estate business. It was Robert Halford who created the foundation upon which the family prospered.

Harry Baker Halford married, in 1891, Miss Ethel Grundy, the youngest daughter of a local auctioneer, John Grundy. They had three children – Leslie Robert, Kathleen and Frank Bernard. Harry Baker was adopted as the Conservative candidate for the council elections of 1907 and was elected Councillor representing St Ann's Ward. In 1912, he was Sheriff of Nottingham. He was a member of the estates, tramways, markets, fairs and old age pensions committees. In addition to his public service, he was a keen sportsman and played local cricket for the Notts Amateurs and football for Beeston and for the Bank and Waverley clubs. He was also Chairman of the Church Football Association in 1907. Like his father Robert, Harry was also appointed a director of Notts County Football Club. He took office on 14 August 1911 but records are not available showing his term of office. Harry Baker died on 30 December 1934; his wife surviving him for over 20 more years.

This then is the family background into which Frank Bernard Halford was born on 7 May 1894, the family then living at No 24 Mapperley Road, Nottingham, which ran along the south side of the grounds of Forest Hall in the north east quarter of the city. Frank and his elder brother attended local schools and also a local dancing school (years later, the fact that Frank had attended these dancing lessons had a major impact on his life) until they each reached the age of thirteen, when they were sent to boarding school. This was Felsted School at Dunmow, Essex, founded in 1564 by Richard Lord Riche, Lord Chancellor of England. By 1907, when Frank entered Elwyn's House, the school had a well established and highly respected engineering department, a facility not readily available at that period of the century when the classical subjects were in the forefront for university entrance. It was one of the very few establishments to provide this, supported by well equipped workshops.

Frank remained at Felsted until December 1910, by which time he was house prefect in the sixth form of the Engineering School and had won the Engineering Prize. He was determined to pursue an engineering career and, on returning to Nottingham with the required passes, took up a place at the Nottingham University College. He commenced a degree course in engineering, but did not stay to take his finals. During his university period, he became a member of the Nottingham and District Motor Cycle Club, annual subscription ten shillings and sixpence (55p) and, at seventeen years of age, began to establish a notable reputation as a competitor in the club's speed and cross-country trials. He acquired various machines, changing from a Martin to a TT Rover and then to a racing Triumph. His father provided the necessary financial support for this fairly dangerous sport. To be able to stand a reasonable chance of success, particularly in the speed events, he was quick to develop the skills of tuning and maintenance to improve the engine performance and road-holding of the machine. By this time he had greatly increased and improved his knowledge of the internal combustion engine and understood its limitations as marketed in 1911-12.

In the 7 May 1912 issue of *Motor Cycling*, there is a report on the Nottingham and District Motor Cycle Club Midland Open Trial covering 150 miles. F B Halford was named as a competitor who passed the first two stages, but did not appear in the list of finishers. Unfortunately, his performance was not recorded nor the type of machine he rode. However, he regularly participated in the sport and this continued into the 1920s.

Ready to race at the White House, Sept 1913
(Ann Spring)

By 1912, the year his father held the office of Sheriff of the City, the family had moved into the *White House* in the village of Edwalton some three-and-a-half miles south-east of the city.

Edwalton was a small and pleasant village containing the stone-built Edwalton Hall, now a country house hotel, and the Church of the Holy Rood which dated from 1166 and purporting to have been built by a knight as a penance for his part in the murder of Thomas à Becket. The *White House* was a pleasant two-storey house of brick. The exterior above the first floor being rough cast finish and painted white and standing in modest grounds. Frank Halford's family and his education reflected a comfortable position in life, which enabled him to enjoy a fair degree of independence and choice in his future occupation.

16

By the time he left university, his mind was set on aviation and he looked for a suitable apprenticeship as entry into this new technical sphere. However, he found that no suitable apprenticeships were available; it was too early in the very limited aviation industry. His father, who was quite horrified by the idea of flying, suggested a motor car course with Daimlers. The young fledgling engineer was impatient to get going and, in the autumn of 1913 at the age of nineteen, left his Edwalton home to go south to the birth place of British aviation – Brooklands – at Weybridge, Surrey.

He decided that entry into an aviation career should commence by learning to fly and so entered this exciting arena with its small number of enthusiasts who were pioneering this new form of transportation. This was to prove very valuable in the coming terrible years of warfare. It also set the seal on Halford's future.

Brother Leslie, on completion of his education at Felsted, returned to join his father in the family estate business until 1914 when he enlisted in the Seaforth Highlanders, later being commissioned in the Sherwood Foresters. He served with great distinction, was wounded ("once or twice" he said), mentioned in despatches and awarded the Military Cross and rose to the rank of Major. In the Second World War, he commanded a battalion of the Home Guard with the rank of Lieutenant-Colonel. After his service in the 1914-1918 War, he returned to join his father and uncle in the family estate agency. Frank and Leslie were never very close and their lives became separated as Frank's path took him into engineering.

The White House, Edwalton   (Patricia Draper)

17

1911 Triumph, 1911 Martini/JAP 1912 Rudge at White House before the Open Speed Trials, Sept 1913   (Ann Spring)

Frank's 1911 Racing Triumph at the White House, Sept 1912 Note: no gearbox (Ann Spring)

Frank with TT Rover – 1911 Notts & District MCC Speed Trials   (Ann Spring)

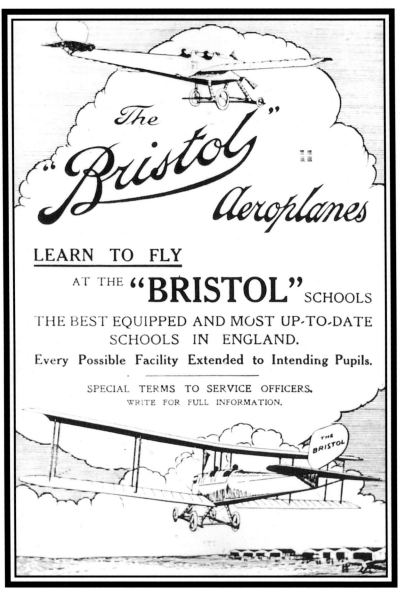

Poster for the British and Colonial Flying School, Brooklands 1913
(Brooklands Museum)

CHAPTER TWO

1913 – Flying at Brooklands

With aviation starting at Brooklands in 1907 when A V Roe built and tested his own design of biplane, flying steadily progressed at the site with others taking up this high-risk activity and, by 1913, aviation was developing at an accelerating pace. Machines were becoming more manoeuvrable and power units somewhat more reliable. This was the year that Adolphe Pegoud looped the loop in France and then at Brooklands. Flying upside-down was referred to by the Press of the time as "aerial acrobatics".

At Brooklands, a number of manufacturers and pioneer aviators had established workshops and flying schools. By 1913, these were the British and Colonial (known also as the Bristol School) plus seven others, namely T O M Sopwith, Vickers, A V Roe, Ducrocq & Lawford, Herbert Spencer, Howard Flanders and Percival. In addition, the War Office – at last taking an interest in this new development of flying with heavier than air machines whilst maintaining their development of balloons and airships at Farnborough – leased a shed at the aerodrome.

Pupils and instructors – September 1913. Warren Merriam at the controls and Frank as passenger   (Ann Spring)

The British and Colonial Flying School was equipped with the Bristol Boxkite as a standard training machine, which had originated in 1910 as a development of the French Henri Farman machine.

Subject to weather conditions, the skies around Brooklands echoed daily with the noise of engines being run up and aircraft flying around the local districts. Pilots under instruction were particularly apprehensive of the perils of the adjacent sewage farm in the event of engine failure or faulty approach when landing. It was to this haunt of enthusiastic activities that Frank Halford presented himself on 6 August 1913 at the Bristol School and, with £75 borrowed from his mother, enrolled as a pupil. In addition to tuition, the fee included insurance for breakages and third-party risks. Fortunately, Halford kept a diary of his tuition (now in the Library of the Royal Aeronautical Society, courtesy of Halford's step-daughter, Mrs Ann Spring) and it is from this the following daily details have been taken.

He was introduced to his instructor, Mr F Warren Merriam, and quickly took his first lesson. This was immediately followed by further tuition from Captains Evans and Jackson. As the weather conditions were good, a further two periods of instruction followed with Lieutenants Lewis and Mead. All these lessons were on the school aircraft, the Boxkite. The following day, Thursday 7 August, he reported to Warren Merriam who took him up to check the all-important weather conditions. All aircraft at this period of early aviation suffered the lack of availability of more powerful engines. This, coupled with problems of stability, made aircraft very susceptible to weather. This meant that flights were restricted to a narrow weather window requiring a careful daily assessment of the weather conditions.

Then followed a lesson with instructor Lt Playfair (in 1915, Playfair, now Captain, commanded B Flight of No 11 Squadron in France). Next Merriam took Halford up to 2000 feet and demonstrated a spiral descent. At this period of early training, all flights were conducted within the boundaries of the Brooklands Aerodrome.

Daily instruction followed during the rest of the month. Halford's diary records the following:-

August 8	Up with Lt Playfair who demonstrated altitude control followed by take-off and landing.
August 11	No flying – too windy and wet.
August 12	With Merriam and had first flight in pilot's seat, getting feel of controls. Later that day flew with Capt Fisher who showed banked turns and vol planes.
August 13 and 14	No flying – unsuitable weather.
August 15	Flew with Merriam as passenger on a test flight. Later flew as pilot to practice circuits.

This pattern continued and by August 29 he was learning figures-of-eight with Merriam in the passenger seat. Merriam was much impressed by this keen young pupil and wrote in his report: *"This pupil has the makings of a very good pilot"*. Then came a period of bad weather which prevented flying from August 30 to September 7.

Flying recommenced on September 8 and Halford was able to do solo circuits. Later that day, as a passenger with Merriam at the controls, they flew over an airship near Weybridge. Lessons continued as the weather conditions allowed, with Halford steadily improving his skills and, on October 14, the Royal Aero Club awarded him Pilot's Certificate No 639. This was then referred to as the pilot's brevet. Flight magazine published his picture and The Nottingham Daily Guardian announced that *"Frank B Halford, younger son of the Sheriff of Nottingham, has qualified for a pilot certificate"*. He became more involved in the flying school's activities including the ever-present need of maintenance of the power units. It is recorded that he spent October 29 and 30 reassembling the Gnome engine for a Boxkite.

Halford was very interested in the racing on the Brooklands track. An entry in the diary dated October 31 recorded the death of Percy Lambert, killed in his Talbot at 10.00am on the track. There is also a note which suggests Halford could have taken a Vauxhall car around the track. Unfortunately, the reference is not clear and no further entries enlighten.

Having obtained his pilot's brevet, he unexpectedly had the opportunity to continue at the Bristol School as a member of the staff. When the assistant instructor was killed, falling out of his aircraft at 1000 feet, Halford applied for, and was accepted, for the job receiving the magnificent salary of twenty-nine shillings and ninepence per week. In addition to instructing, the job included maintenance of the Gnome engines which powered the School's Boxkites. He started the day at 4.00am with tuition of pupils until 7.00am (the wind preventing further flying until the evening) then maintenance work during the day. Resources were meagre and improvisation was the order of the

Frank at the controls of the 50hp Gnome Bristol Boxkite, Brooklands, September 1913   (Ann Spring)

23

Halford was awarded his pilot's certificate on 14 October 1913. Pictured here at the White House. (Ann Spring)

day. A year of this improved his knowledge of engines and their shortcomings and daily flying as an instructor provided invaluable experience. He thoroughly enjoyed his life at the School.

On November 17, he flew as passenger with Harry Hawker in the new racing Sopwith Tabloid and they reached over 100mph. This machine was a biplane designed by Harry Hawker and Fred Sigrist and fitted with an 80hp Gnome engine. Hawker was a close friend of T O M Sopwith and test-flew his aircraft from 1912 until his death in 1921. Halford photographed the Tabloid at Brooklands and appended the following brief facts after his flight with Hawker: *"With a passenger plus 5½ hours of fuel on board, the maximum speed was 92mph, minimum speed 36.9mph and climbing performance 1,200 feet per minute"*.

By December, he was appointed instructor to replace Mr Skene who left to continue his career elsewhere. *The Nottingham Daily Guardian* again recorded the news of the local boy on 19 January 1914: *"Frank Halford has been appointed assistant pilot instructor for the Bristol Aeroplane Company Flying School at Brooklands, Surrey. He is not yet 20 and is the youngest flying instructor in the country"*. The next month, Halford was in his home town news again. The Nottingham Guardian of February 16 confirmed he had been appointed assistant manager and chief instructor of the Bristol Flying School.

In March 1914, Halford's first pupil, a Lt F B Binney RFA, successfully received his pilot's certificate. March 17 was a day of fine weather and a great occasion for Halford. (In August 1914, Binney joined the Royal Flying Corps (RFC) and, by September, was Flight Commander with No 12 Squadron in France. On September 25, he was wounded and crashed behind enemy lines, surviving as a prisoner of war).

Halford had a visit from his mother and sister to Brooklands and took them for a seven mile flight, reaching an altitude of 1000 feet. It is said, *"the ladies much enjoyed the experience"*. His mother was always very supportive of this career.

The 1913-14 diary, in addition to the handwritten recording of progress of flying lessons, was supplemented with cut-out extracts from the *Flight* and *Aeroplane* weekly magazines. It was the practice of these publications to list in detail all activities and every daily flight by named pupils and instructors undertaken by the then few flying schools around the country. The fact that Halford inserted these in his diary meant that an accurate and detailed record exists of not only his own training but a picture of the steady increase in the number of people taking up the art of flying and the skills required to operate these early aircraft. The diary is scattered with very well drawn pen caricatures of friends enlivened with comments. His fascination with racing is shown, in particular by an

Harry Hawker at Brooklands, 1913
(Ann Spring)

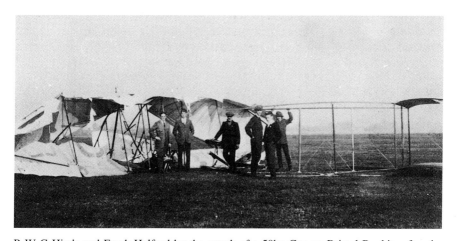

R W G Hinds and Frank Halford by the wreck of a 50hp Gnome Bristol Boxkite after the propeller burst at 100 feet. Hinds, the pilot, was unhurt. Brooklands, 19 October 1913
(Ann Spring)

Mrs Billing, C P P Pizey and F Warren Merriam, Brooklands 1913
(Ann Spring)

ink sketch purporting to be himself racing at Brooklands on a 70hp Gnome motorcycle and entitled, *"FBH racing under Members Bridge at over 100mph".* Wishful thinking at that time!

Halford continued at the Bristol School until August 1914 when, as a result of negotiations with the Hon Hugh Fortescue Locke-King, owner of the Brooklands site, and agreements with the various flying schools operating from there, General Hugh Trenchard obtained the occupancy of the entire site on behalf of the Government for the Royal Flying Corps. The deal included all aircraft, equipment, hangars and even a local public house, the landlord including its stock. Brooklands was taken over, lock stock and barrel, and the deal was finalised by the last week of August. It has been said that Brooklands was 'purchased' by the Government, but no record of such a sale, or re-purchase after the War by Locke-King, exists in the Brooklands archives. It has been assumed that the Government acquired its use of the site by lease. The RFC were in desperate need of every flying instructor available and all the civilian instructors and certified pilots were required to provide training for the RFC expansion, now under war status. In 1912, Trenchard himself, at the age of thirty-nine, had learnt to fly at Mr T O M Sopwith's School of Flying at Brooklands and successfully earned his brevet, ticket No 270, in August of that year. He trained on a Maurice Farman machine under his instructor, Copland Perry.

As previously mentioned, the senior instructor at the time Halford underwent his training was F Warren Merriam. He was the most respected instructor at Brooklands in 1914. Later, he became instructor for the Royal Naval Air Service (RNAS) and the Royal Flying Corps and Royal Air Force. After a distinguished career, he died at the age of 76 in 1956.

Halford had received the best of training and was in his element in the prevailing atmosphere of Brooklands aviation. Populated as it was by a crowd of lively, enthusiastic and courageous young men, he joined the crowd and was immediately accepted as a kindred spirit. His basic knowledge of engineering and motorcycle racing gave him a lead in involvement in aircraft mechanics as well as piloting. Where better to meet with fellow enthusiasts than in the convivial atmosphere of the Blue Bird restaurant to enjoy the camaraderie and discuss the events of the day. The free exchange of problems encountered provided a source of valuable knowledge, contributing to the advancement of this wonderful new media of flight.

The famous Blue Bird Restaurant, Brooklands 1913
(Ann Spring)

It was in a converted hangar, once used by Martin and Handasyde, that Eardley Billing, with his wife and daughter, created the Blue Bird restaurant, "Popular food at popular prices" providing what became a much appreciated facility by all who worked, flew and visited the Brooklands flying grounds. Eardley Billing, was the brother of Pemberton Billing MP, who founded the Supermarine Aviation Company in 1913 and later linked with Vickers at Brooklands in originating the Supermarine Schneider Trophy racing seaplane. Eardley Billing himself designed and built his own aircraft and also what was probably the first aircraft simulator. Later, in 1917, when the site was occupied by the Royal Flying Corps and the Blue Bird restaurant had been used as the canteen, it was totally destroyed by fire.

From 1910 to August 1914, a total of 318 civilian pupils had been trained at Brooklands, nearly twice the number that had been trained at Hendon over the same period.

The Bristol Boxkite

This biplane, created in 1910, was a copy of the Henri Farman machine.

The dimensions were the same but it had more refined metal fittings.

The first two constructed at the Filton works were to drawings by George Challenger in June 1910. They were fitted with either 50hp Gregoire 4-cylinder engines or 50hp ENV 8-cylinder engines. These were water-cooled units.

There were 16 standard Boxkites completed by the end of 1910 and the advertised cost, in 1911, was £943. The Bristol works continued production until 1914; the total built was 76.

The Flying School at Brooklands was allocated:-
Machine No 7   with a 50hp Gnome rotary engine
Machine No 11
Machine No 16   rebuilt after a crash
Machine No 29   delivered to Brooklands in February 1911

School machines had twin rudders and the Gnome engine was then the standard.

1913 Bristol Boxkite – single rudder   (Brooklands Museum)

Bristol Boxkite twin rudder – as used at the Flying School   (Brooklands Museum)

Major Halford RFC/RAF 1918-19 (Ann Spring)

CHAPTER THREE

1914 – 1919 The AID and the RFC

At the outbreak of the war, Halford had completed what was for him an outstanding and exciting twelve months. It was on 6 August 1913, he had started his training as a pilot. As the year progressed, he obtained his certificate, became an instructor and then had taken on the duties of assistant manager of the Bristol Flying School. He was twenty years of age.

As a result of his experience and following the takeover of Brooklands by the RFC, he was approached by Captain R K Bagnall-Wild, Chief Inspector of Engines at the Aeronautical Inspection Directorate (AID) at Farnborough (formed in 1913) who suggested he apply for the post of engine examiner. Remuneration would be fifty shillings per 48-hour week, plus six shillings per day subsistence allowance. Halford accepted with alacrity. He jumped at the chance of working with aircraft engines and contributing to the war and the RFC.

The responsibilities of the AID included overseeing design and development, quality control and progressing delivery of orders for aircraft and engines. It was at Farnborough that Halford first met a 2nd-Lt Geoffrey de Havilland RFC, who was temporarily appointed Inspector of Aircraft whilst recovering from injuries suffered during testing a BS1 single-seat scout plane of his own design. It was de Havilland's younger brother, Hereward, also in the RFC, who introduced them.

A resumé of the political and military inaction which preceded the eventual formation of the RFC records the state of the Air Arm when Halford entered the Service. The serious lack of an extensive Air Arm at the commencement of the War resulting from lack of political decision and the negative attitude to aviation by the Army and Navy, had delayed the formation of a third Service. It had been in 1911 that Lord Haldane, Secretary of State for War, had made strong recommendation for the creation of an Aeronautical Arm which should consist of a Military Wing, Naval Wing and a Central Flying School. The 1911-12 Treasury appropriation for the proposed Service was barely half a million pounds. On 13 April 1912, a Royal Warrant was issued for the formation of the Royal Flying Corps and the Service came into being on 13 May 1912. The Under Secretary of State for War, Colonel J F B Seely, highlighted Britain's position when he briefed Brigadier David Henderson, Director of Military Training, stating, *"At the present, in this country, there is in the Army about eleven flying men and in the Navy about eight. Whereas in France, there are two hundred and sixty-three. We are somewhat behind"*.

The result of financial limitations and controversy over the specific duties of the RFC impacted on decisions as to the types of aircraft to be put into production, resulting in a depleted force available when War started. It had also delayed the creation of designs and manufacture of aircraft in what was a fledgling industry. The aircraft industry in Britain consisted of a number of small constructors, most of whom were pioneering individuals who were not in a position to produce aircraft in any significant quantity. This had its effect on the aero-engine market. By 1914, there were few British companies producing engines specifically for aircraft. Among these were:-

Vertical or Vee engines:

ABC	water-cooled 4-, 6-, 8-, 12-cylinder at 45, 85,
(All British Engine Co)	115, 170 bhp
Beardmore	water-cooled 4- and 6-cylinder at 40, 65, 80,
(Austro Daimler)	120 bhp
Green	water-cooled 4- and 6-cylinder at 30, 60,
	120 bhp
Sunbeam	water-cooled 8- and 12-cylinder at 150, 225
	bhp
Wolseley	water-cooled 8-cylinder at 90, 120 bhp

Radial and Rotary engines:

Anzani	radial air-cooled 3-, 6-, 10-cylinder at 30,
	45, 125 bhp
Dudbridge Iron Works	radial water-cooled 7-, 9-, 14-cylinder at 90,
(Salmson)	120, 200bhp
Gwynnes	rotary air-cooled 7-cylinder at 60, 80 bhp
(Clerget)	

Both Britain and France were not manufacturing magnetos and were buying from Germany. The outbreak of war denied them this source and both countries had to find out how to make them. This was just one of the problems facing the provision of aircraft. In the later part of 1914, the British Government placed orders with M L Magnetos of Coventry to produce a modified version of the imported Bosch magneto. The company went into successful production and many thousands were supplied for aircraft engines.

Up to this time, most aircraft produced for the Service were to the design of the Royal Aircraft Factory, which came into being in 1909 as the Army Aircraft Factory. This arose out of reorganising the Balloon Company of the Royal Engineers at Farnborough using civilian staff. In 1912, it was renamed the Royal Aircraft Factory. On the formation of the Royal Air Force in 1918, it again was renamed and became the Royal Aircraft Establishment.

When, thanks to the efforts of Trenchard, then commanding the Service in France, the RFC had identified its role, it enabled aircraft designers to concentrate on specific designs and this led to the establishment of engine requirements. As Britain was not well placed to design and produce engines of the types required within the time available in wartime, contracts were placed from 1914 onwards with the following foreign supplies:

1914 Gnome, LeRhone, Hispano-Suiza, Renault, Berliett (Mercedes)
1915 Anzani, Delanney Rellenille (Clerget & Hispano), Darracq (LeRhone)
1916 Aries (Hispano)
1917 Clerget Blin, Canton Unne, Brassier (Hispano), DFP (Hispano), Fires Lille (Hispano), Peugeot (Hispano)
1918 Lorraine Dietrich, Salmson (Clerget)

It is interesting to note that the number of firms building the Hispano-Suiza under licence gives credence to Halford's recommendation of this power unit as recorded later in this chapter.

To return to British aero-engine production, of existing firms William Beardmore had the manufacturing capacity and skills to make a significant contribution to wartime needs. During the war, William Beardmore

Halford pilot in an SE4, Farnborough 1914   (Ann Spring)

33

companies were producing marine vessels, armaments, airships and aircraft (a total of 650 aircraft was produced). Beardmore were eminently suited to undertake additional aero-engine production and Halford was later to become very involved with this company in the course of his duties in the AID and RFC.

As the war progressed, and in parallel with aircraft development, aero-engines were improving in power, lightness and reliability. Types of engines were generally of the air-cooled rotary or water-cooled in-line vertical. The majority did not exceed 80 to 100 bhp. The attraction of the rotary engine was its compact crankcase and corresponding lightness, although a power loss in the order of 25% due to windage of the rotating cylinder mass had to be accepted. There was also the advantage of a much quicker warm-up time enabling aircraft to be airborne with a minimum of delay and the avoidance of the effects of winter conditions on water-cooled units. During the war, aero-engine manufacture grew out of being the specialised experimentation of a few into a national precision industry.

The RFC had great difficulty in providing squadrons to go to France in support of Kitchener's army and, at the same time, to provide for home defence against enemy bombers and Zeppelin attack. Only four squadrons of serviceable aircraft were available to go to the Front on 13 August and these were made up by an assortment of types and corresponding assortment of engines (Appendix III) most of which were of foreign design and supply. This situation brought to the fore the urgent need of the services of the few

Lieutenant RFC, 21 May 1915   (Ann Spring)

34

experienced people available to identify the problems which active service and greatly increased production would undoubtedly highlight.

Halford's duties were to assess the suitability, performance and reliability of the aero-engines in the field and the effectiveness of operating under war conditions. This required that he go to France and would not be permitted to do so as a civilian. He applied to join the RFC and on the 30 August 1914 he completed Attestation No 1645 for short service (one year with the colours, but this was conditional to the length of the war). He gave his trade as 'foreman artificer' and entered the Service that day as an NCO. Such was the urgent need of his skills, he was posted to France fourteen days later on 12 September with orders from the War Office to inspect and report on the French aero-engines currently supplied to the RFC. On the 18 December, he was gazetted honorary lieutenant. He was not attached to a squadron, or in fact to any unit in the field, but reported to Bagnall-Wild at Farnborough as his IE2 to Bagnell-Wild's IE1. Visits to squadrons, French engine manufacturers and to the RFC Engine Repair Shop at Pont de l'Arche near Rouen resulted in a series of reports which established the problems facing the Service in their efforts to keep aircraft in the air.

The Engine Repair Shop (ERS) was a remarkable and successful organisation and greatly responsible for improving engine reliability and power output. It provided a fruitful source from which to obtain well detailed information regarding engine shortcomings, both in design and under battle operations. It started in 1914 in a converted boot factory where the RFC set up permanent workshops for repair and overhaul of aero-engines. Initially, it was under the command of Major A D Carden, assisted by Lieutenant R H Verney. At the end of the year, the unit had three officers and 100 men. By the end of the war, it employed 100 officers, 4500 men and 500 women. It had become a self-contained and self-supporting community with full manufacturing and testing facilities. In April 1915, a young lieutenant, L F R Fell, was transferred from Farnborough to Pont de l'Arche and he was to provide influential direction, not only of improving methods of repair work but also inaugurating design improvements which produced higher power output and great improvements in reliability which increased hours between servicing and successful in keeping aircraft operational.

When Halford returned to Farnborough following an initial tour of six months of the RFC field operations and finalising his reports on the French engines, he was joined by a new arrival, Lieutenant G P Bulman who filled the post of IE3. They started a friendship which was to last the rest of Halford's life. George Bulman was destined to become Director of Engine Development and Production at the Ministry of Aircraft Production during WW2. They worked closely together and with many further visits to France created an excellent co-operation with pilots and ground crews at squadron establishments, the ERS and French suppliers.

At this time, there was general disquiet among pilots who were highly critical of their machines and in particular with the power unit under the heavy strain of combat usage; especially the unreliability of the Gnome Monosoupape engine in 1914. It was not until the spring of 1915 that modifications were effective in overcoming these problems. The Clerget rotary engine was also beset with troubles and had a life of only fifteen hours. Because of this, the introduction of the new Vickers fighter was delayed. This was a serious setback in the effort to combat the success of the new German Fokker fighter (the Eindecker EI and EII, a design very similar to the French Morane-Saulnier monoplane) now appearing in increasing numbers. This was so successful at the time it became known as the 'Fokker Scourge'. In addition to heavy losses of pilots in combat, too many aircrew were lost due to mechanical failures. The results of the field work of Halford and Bulman, coupled with information feeding back from the ERS, enabled the AID to make recommendations of amendments and redesign to the War Office which initiated instructions to engine suppliers and service orders to the field units. A general improvement in engine reliability was achieved.

The length of time required to effect changes and to get new and more powerful engines into service was explained by Captain Maurice Baring, ADC to General Trenchard, and recorded by a note in his diary:

"It may be asked why we have not got the equivalent of Fokkers in great quantities by this time and the answer is that in aviation during the War everything was a compromise between progress and supply. As it took more than nine months for anything new in the shape of a machine or an engine to be available in any quantity, it generally happened that by the time a machine or an engine or the spare parts of both were available in sufficient quantities the engine or machine or spare parts in question by that time were out of date."

What must be remembered is that engines which were an established design and had been in use for some time before the war were now being produced in much increased quantities, in many cases by contractors with no previous experience of aero-engines and the precision engineering essential to meet production requirements.

During a visit to the ERS, Halford had the opportunity to examine the 180 hp Hispano-Suiza engine newly introduced and fitted to the SE5a and SPAD aircraft. The engine had been stripped for overhaul. He was considerably impressed with the design and noted its features. On return to the UK, he submitted a report and recommendation to the War Office to purchase a licence to manufacture. His enquiries had indicated that the French were prepared to negotiate at a very advantageous figure. However, the recommendations of a junior officer were not accepted much to his chagrin

HQ staff AID, Farnborough 1915 (Ann Spring) Front row L to R: H P Philpot, G P Bulman, A P Thurston, Capt Bagnall-Wild, Col Fulton, F B Halford, Mr Ringwood

and when, in 1916, a licence was obtained it was at a considerably greater cost. Orders were then placed with the Wolseley Company to manufacture the Hispano which was then called the Viper.

When at the ERS, L F R Fell – now Captain – reviewed the Hispano-Suiza and incorporated improvements to increase power output. This took the form of using high-compression light-alloy pistons and amending the top of the cylinder bores to raise compression from 5:1 to 5.6:1 and changing the carburettor. This resulted in a power output of 208 hp. Fell had brought to the ERS his experience at the AID who had, in conjunction with the National Physical Laboratory and the Royal Aircraft Establishment, been developing the use of light alloys. The new pistons were cast in the ERS foundry.

Hispano-Suiza were producing three models – a 180 hp direct-drive, a 220 hp and 300 hp geared-drive. These engines were designed with an innovative aluminium cylinder block with steel liners. Halford maintained his enthusiasm for this engine, keeping abreast of its development. When later he was seconded to Beardmores he incorporated a number of Hispano design features to increase power output of the Beardmore engine.

His visits to France ceased in May 1915 when his experience was needed on the home front. The Government were much concerned over the threat of bombing raids by the Zeppelins, which could fly with impunity at altitudes of 16-20,000 feet, heights beyond the reach of any aircraft in current service.

Urgent steps had to be taken to find engines powerful enough to overcome these limitations and provide aircraft to give better defence than that available from anti-aircraft guns. Parallel with this, more powerful engines were also required to equip bombers capable of bombing targets in Germany.

On 2 November 1915, he was promoted to honorary captain and was sent to the Arrol-Johnston factory at Dumfries, a subsidiary of the William Beardmore Company, to assist in developing the Austro-Daimler engine being built under licence. The essential requirement was for a substantial increase in power from the 120 hp of the initial design. He had the able help of T C Pullinger, Beardmore's chief engineer. As a result of their efforts, power was increased by 30% to 160 hp. This was achieved by changes which could be rapidly incorporated without halting production, such as twin carburettors and dual ignition. It was during this period at Arrol-Johnston that Halford came to know a young draughtsman apprentice named John Brodie, who impressed him with his enthusiasm for design. Some years later, Brodie came to London as the first member of Halford's consultancy staff. Brodie clearly recalled his first meeting with this handsome young RFC captain who appeared to live and breathe engines and inspired everyone on the design team.

Galloway BHP 6-cylinder engine   (Rolls-Royce Heritage Trust)

With many ideas for development, which he discussed with Pullinger and without War Office approval, they started on a new design which became known as the BHP – Beardmore, Halford, Pullinger. There was a considerable amount of Hispano-Suiza influence incorporated into the design including the use of a cast aluminium monoblock for each group of three cylinders and steel cylinder liners screwed into the block. The cylinder head was designed with a single large nickel-steel inlet valve and two smaller tungsten-steel exhaust valves. This replaced the initial design of a single inlet and exhaust valve and with a bore of 145mm and 190mm stroke and with two Zenith carburettors, a power increase of up to 200 hp at 1400 rpm was expected. Manufacture of a prototype engine was completed and, following test-bed running, a BHP was installed in a DH4 aircraft for flight test. The aircraft attained a speed of 111 mph at 10,000 feet. In January, the engine was installed in the new DH9.

By June 1916, a new company – The Galloway Engine Company Ltd – had been set up with a new factory at Dumfries to produce the BHP. With the success of the DH4, orders for 100 engines per week were placed, but with Arrol-Johnston at full capacity producing the Beardmore engine Siddeley-Deasy in Coventry were called in to help meet the requirements for the BHP in addition to Galloway's production.

Halford's use of an aluminium cylinder block with screwed-in steel liners, cast-iron cylinder heads and sheet steel water jackets had created initial problems with porosity and machining of the aluminium monoblocks. Siddeley, however, changed the cylinder heads to aluminium which screwed onto the steel liners and the water jackets were also in aluminium. Giving 230 hp at 1400 rpm, the dry weight per horsepower was 2.96 lb. The Siddeley-modified engine was then called the Puma. Production continued beyond the date of the Armistice and a total of 6000 was made. Meanwhile, the Galloway Engine Company with Halford, and Harry Ricardo as consultant, designed the 12-cylinder BHP Atlantic of 500 hp with the same bore and stroke of 145mm and 190mm and with a dry weight per horsepower of 2.42 lb. This was fitted to only one DH9a aircraft after a production of 72 of this type of engine.

While Halford was engaged in the BHP development early in 1916, he was summoned by Bagnall-Wild to visit a gentleman at Walton on Thames, Surrey, who was engaged on a most interesting development of high-powered aero-engines. Harry Ricardo had his workshop in the garden of his home and it was here that Halford was introduced to the design and watched a demonstration of a single-cylinder test unit. This development had began in 1914-15 by Ricardo as a result of a commission from Commander Briggs RNAS whose idea was to install a large power unit in the hull of a flying boat with separate drives to two wing-mounted propellers, the purpose being to carry out long-range anti-submarine patrols. At that time, a 'large' aero-engine would be around 160 hp. Ricardo's design of a 300 hp 12-cylinder 30-degree-vee supercharged engine was well advanced by the summer of 1915 when instructions were received from the Admiralty to cancel the project.

This design was remembered by Harry Hetherington, a Cambridge friend of Ricardo, now attached to the Aeronautical Inspection Directorate, when the question of a high-powered engine suitable for higher altitudes was being considered. Hetherington brought this to the attention of Bagnall-Wild who despatched Halford to investigate and report back. Ricardo's method of supercharging was to introduce an amount of inert exhaust gas and clean air to the crown of the piston. This had the effect of diluting the mixture at low altitudes, but as altitude was increased more mixture became available and between 10,000 and 20,000 feet it provided an improved thermal cycle and tests were proving an increase of efficiency of up to 34% and fuel consumption fell to 0.465 lb per bhp. Halford was impressed by the design. From that initial meeting, a mutual respect and eventually a lifelong friendship and technical collaboration became established.

After reporting favourably to Bagnall-Wild, approval to continue the project was given and Halford instructed to find a suitable company to develop the details and undertake manufacture. He approached T C Pullinger at Beardmore, now chief engineer and technical director, for whose technical abilities he had great respect. Beardmore's work in developing the BHP 230

Galloway BHP Atlantic 12-cylinder 500bhp   (Rolls-Royce Heritage Trust)

Siddeley Puma 6-cylinder 230bhp   (Rolls-Royce Heritage Trust)

hp engine had added to their experience in aero-engine production. Halford brought Pullinger to Walton on Thames where drawings were available for examination and the test unit run. Pullinger had some reservations on reviewing the design, as it was based on the use of large aluminium castings, and he suggested using separate cylinder blocks. This meant considerable redrawing. On getting approval of the appointment of Beardmore as detailer and manufacturer, Halford offered Ricardo the services of a young AID draughtsman named Dennis Plunkett who, on arrival, was established at Ricardo's London office to assist in producing the revised design, after which he returned to the AID. (After the war, Plunkett rejoined Ricardo and continued with the company until his retirement in 1963. He died in 1993 at the age of 99).

The redesign was sent to Beardmore for detail drawings to be made but, after some weeks, it became clear that little was happening. By the spring of 1916, Ricardo became involved in other projects and Halford was left to pressure Beardmore to perform. He was unable to get them to progress with the desired urgency. It appeared to be due to trouble within the Beardmore management. It therefore, became necessary to reconsider the manufacturing source.

Halford contacted Edwin Orde, a director of Armstrongs, who had been instrumental in establishing a light-engineering department to supply, as subcontractor, small high-precision parts for gun fittings and aero-engines. Orde was eager to tackle the manufacture of the supercharged engine and brought the two men in charge of the department, Le Mesurier and Everet, to meet Halford and Ricardo, following which a contract was placed with

41

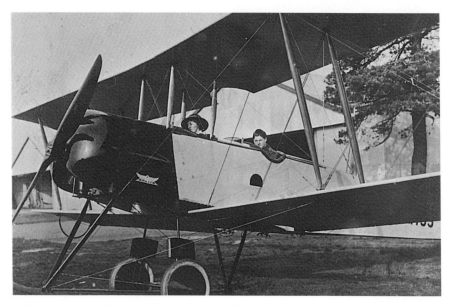

Halford with sister, Kathleen, in an Avro 504 military aircraft (note bomb racks under wings), Farnborough 1916   (Ann Spring)

Armstrong for the manufacture of six prototype engines. By the spring of 1917, these became known as the RHA (Ricardo Halford Armstrong). Two engines were completed before the date of the Armistice, with the remaining four near completion. The type-test of the first engine showed an output of 260 hp without supercharging and 360 hp with supercharged air. The initial design meant that the height above the crankshaft was such as to severely obscure the pilot's forward view. The solution was arrived at by redesign to invert the engine and it was installed in a DH4. Flight tests in the de Havilland aircraft at Farnborough proved successful. By this time, the Armistice brought further development to an end and the engine joined other redundant projects. Although the engine had not been used in active service, a great deal had been learnt in the process of designing and testing a large horsepower supercharged unit and this became of great importance some few years later.

To return to the BHP project, a decision by the Directorate of Military Aeronautics to standardise the high-power engines for bombers resulted in the selection of a short list of four engine designs and, during January 1917, the Advisory Committee for Aeronautics – Internal Combustion Engine Sub-Committee met to determine which of the four designs should be selected for immediate manufacture. These were the Hispano-Suiza, the BHP and two Sunbeam engines.

The Sub-Committee called representatives from the companies whose designs were being considered to appear before them in support of their designs. Captain Halford and Mr Ricardo attended on behalf of the BHP, answering numerous questions to satisfy the Committee of the suitability of the design submitted and the results of both test-bed and flight tests of the prototype power unit. The result was that production orders were issued for a modified Atlantic which used the Puma cylinder block and was renamed the BHP Pacific.

It is interesting to note that at the meeting, which was held on 12 January 1917, reference was minuted that the work on a supercharged version of the BHP was carried out by Messrs Engine Patents Ltd (Captain Halford and Mr Ricardo). This was the company set up by Ricardo and it was not registered until June 1917. These meetings established Halford's close involvement with Ricardo and did much to confirm Halford's position as a recognised aero-engine designer and establish his future career in the industry.

The measure of the rapid wartime growth of the British aero-engine manufacture can be assessed by the fact that a labour force of 20,000 was

BHP Pacific 12-cylinder 550bhp   (Rolls-Royce Heritage Trust)

employed by the summer of 1916.

In the first week of April 1917, Henderson wrote an assessment and review of the aerial situation on the Western Front in which he stated that the SE5 single-seater fighter was superior to any German machine but the delay in producing large numbers is due almost entirely to the delays in engine production:

"... Only now are we getting British-made engines equal to those which the Germans have had for the last eighteen months, with the exception of the Rolls-Royce engine, of which the supply has always been limited. The high-powered British engines, however, have now reached the production stage and the quantities delivered are expected to increase week by week."

In May 1918, Halford – now Honorary Major – was appointed assistant to A E L Charlton, Head of Aircraft Engine Production at the Air Ministry. However, the Air Ministry appointment was not to his taste, being too far removed from the heart of design and bordering on being a civil servant in uniform. On 7 November 1918, his honorary rank was substantiated but, on 24 February 1919, he relinquished his commission and returned to civilian life. In 1914, he had been awarded the Mons Star and in February 1917 mentioned in Home Service Despatches.

It was while he was attached to the Air Ministry in mid 1918 and living in London, he took the opportunity to enjoy the theatres. One evening, passing a theatre staging a performance by the Pavlova Ballet Company he saw a familiar name billed as the prima ballerina. He was able to get a seat and watch the performance. The familiar name was indeed that of a young lady he last met whilst attending dancing lessons during school days in his home town of Nottingham. Following the performance, he sent a note backstage to Monica Bevan reminding her of those earlier dancing lessons and inviting her to supper. Monica was happy to accept.

Monica's consuming passion was ballet and, starting at a very young age, she attended the Gilman Ballet School in Nottingham. By the age of ten, she suffered from acute bronchitis and medical advice was that to continue dancing would kill or cure. Fortunately, the latter prevailed. It was in 1906 that Miss Bevan, a fourteen-year-old pupil, had assisted in teaching ballroom dancing to a class of boys from a local school. Thirteen-year-old Frank Halford was one of the class. Now, twelve years later, by good fortune they met again. Their friendship quickly blossomed into courtship and, in March 1919, Monica married the handsome RFC major. On leaving the Service, Halford took up a career with Harry Ricardo at the time Ricardo was establishing his own organisation.

As a final note on the war, in which Halford made a significant contribution to aero-engine development, the Government had placed orders for engines from August 1914 to December 1918 for a total of 87,629.

Actual deliveries were reduced to 41,044 by cancellations issued when the Armistice was declared.

Appendix II shows the variety of power units ordered from all sources and the numbers delivered annually.

By the end of hostilities, the RFC – now the RAF – had on strength 27,333 officers, 263,837 other ranks and 22,647 aircraft which provided 200 Operation Squadrons and 109 Training Squadrons.

Harry R Ricardo returning from a visit to the USA in 1932 (Author)

CHAPTER FOUR

1919 – 1922 Ricardo and Company

Sir Harry Ricardo LLD FRS was born in London in 1885 and took an engineering degree at Cambridge University in 1907. He had been involved in the design of internal combustion engines, even before his University days, and was particularly interested in the means of improving the efficiency of the combustion process. An interest which led to prominence in this particular area of engine design. In 1916, he was responsible for the design of the engine fitted to the first tanks. These engines, initially of 150 hp and later 225 hp, had to be free of visible exhaust smoke and avoid stalling on the battlefield. To attain this Ricardo needed better fuels than those which the War Office provided. In 1917, he put his plea to the War Office committee responsible for fuel allocation for a better grade to be allocated which would reduce pre-detonation (or 'pinking') in the tank engines and give more power. This request was refused so he asked for benzole or benzene; this was also refused. The committee chairman was Robert Waley Cohen, a director of Shell Transport, who after the meeting took Ricardo aside and wanted to know more about benzole and detonation.

As a result of their discussions, it was arranged that Shell would send samples of its different fuels to Ricardo for evaluation. The results of his tests showed a particular grade from Borneo gave consistently better results. Waley Cohen engaged Ricardo as a consultant to start a continuing programme of fuel development and, as described later, this led to the advent of racing fuels.

In February 1919, Halford returned to civilian life and needed to find employment. He had determined to pursue a design career and the opportunity to do so presented itself when Harry Ricardo decided to set up his own company and invited Halford to join him with a few friends. Initially registered as Engine Patents Limited its name was soon changed to Ricardo and Company. It was organised into two management groups: Financial and Administration/Technical. The second group consisted of Ricardo, Hetherington, Thornycroft and Halford. Halford found that instead of being engaged in design, Ricardo wished him to look after client relationships and the immediate need was to explore and assess the American automobile and aero-engine market with the object of negotiating the use of Ricardo patents under licence and royalty agreements and to explore the feasibility of establishing an organisation to represent Ricardo's interests in the United States.

Very shortly after joining the new company, Halford, with his wife, set sail for Cleveland, USA, where he opened an office. During their initial period in the United States, they stayed with the President of the Aluminum Company of America (ALCOA) who was most hospitable and, although the Prohibition Act was still in force, this household enjoyed a remarkably good stock of alcoholic liquor. Halford had lengthy discussions with ALCOA on the future use of aluminium in the design of aero-engines, initially to maximise the use of light weight material. However, this did not develop into production for some years.

By the time the Halfords entered the new decade of the twenties, Monica realised the difficulties she faced in adjusting to the American scene and this was exacerbated by the confirmation that she was pregnant. She decided to return to England to have the baby and so, in early 1920, she sailed west to east across the Atlantic again. At Hampstead, London, on 26 March, daughter Patricia was born. Apart from short visits to England, Halford continued his efforts in the USA for a total of two-and-a-half years until the slump struck America and there was little hope of further business. The decision of his wife to return to England to have the baby and the long periods of separation this caused, particularly as Monica did not wish to return to America with their new-born child, made it a most difficult relationship for them both. Halford was in no position to abandon his commitment to Ricardo. It indicated there were early problems with the marriage.

In the period he operated in the USA, Halford did achieve success but notably not with Henry Ford who wanted to know how much Ford would be paid to use the Ricardo slipper piston and turbulent-head patent designs. Halford returned to the UK in 1921 to find that here also, a post-war slump was severely affecting the country. He now joined Ricardo in their London office and became involved in the development work that Ricardo had started in 1917 on behalf of the Shell Company.

Ricardo had been investigating the effects of various additives to petrol which, at that time, had an octane value around 50 for commercial fuel and 60 for aviation spirit. This limited compression ratios to about 5 to 1. By using petrol from the Borneo oil fields, which had a high anti-knock value and using a cut from distillations of higher volatility in the alcohol range, compression ratios could be raised to 6 to 1 and an increase of around 10% in power was possible. From this line of research Ricardo had the idea of developing a higher-octane fuel specifically for use in racing motorcycles and cars. Ricardo has stated that he was further encouraged to develop the 'racing fuel' when the Brooklands Organising Committee considered banning supercharged engines and engines of unlimited cylinder capacity at Brooklands races, but there was no restriction on types of fuel which could be used. Shell and the Distillers Company agreed to produce a small amount of this fuel to Ricardo's prescription. It was, of course, expensive fuel to buy.

The Triumph Ricardo motorcycle

When Halford returned to the UK in April 1921, he took up his pre-war sport of motorcycle racing. He participated in many of the Brooklands meetings, as detailed in a later chapter. He was riding a 500cc single-cylinder Triumph with side valves and compression similar to his pre-war machine and, although the performance was not wonderful, he did well in handicap races due to skilful riding. In July, he collaborated with Ricardo's racing programme and agreed to ride the Triumph fitted with Ricardo's new engine. At this stage, the Ricardo engine, an advanced design, had a steel cylinder barrel, spigotted into a cast-iron head held down by five studs and a metal-to-metal joint. The head contained four valves, two inlet and two exhaust – the pairs being angled at 90 degrees. Inlet valves were masked, the first motorcycle engine with this feature, by slightly recessing the valve seating in the cylinder head. This meant that the first part of the lift and the last part of the drop of the cam are almost ineffective. The valves can be raised from, and returned to, their seats gently, the effective lift and drop being very sharp. Noise and stress on the valve operating gear is thus reduced. Bore and stroke were 80.5mm and 98mm. A fully-skirted piston were discarded and a Ricardo slipper-type used. During the season, various modifications were tried, one of which was a water-cooled cylinder head with a radiator forming the front part of the fuel tank. This was raced in the 500cc Solo Championship at Brooklands on 21 October. It was not a successful change and was abandoned. The Mark IIB engine was run satisfactorily on the test-bed at the Shoreham works on the first of May 1921 producing 18 bhp when fitted with a Solex carburettor, but when raced at Brooklands on the 3rd gave a poor performance and, on stripping the engine at Shoreham on the 5th, the cause was identified as a very badly worn inlet rocker finger.

The Mark IIA engine was run on the test-bed fitted with a Zenith carburettor, but poor results were obtained. The carburettor was changed to a special small-sized Amal and, after further carburettor experiments, the engine was fitted in the first TT frame. Power output, taken at 3900 rpm, and trying out various jet and choke settings, gave 16, 18, 19 and 20 bhp. By 20 May, efforts to increase power resulted in trouble with the cylinder head. The head was removed from the Mark IIA engine and was sectioned. This revealed a crack through the bar between the exhaust valve seats and involved the slot through which a holding-down bolt passed. This was identified as being due to overheating and a problem found in other types of engine, but with the common fault that it occurred when using two exhaust valves in a cast-iron head. The development work continued on the racing

Triumph Ricardo 500cc production road model, 1922   (Author)

Mark II engine and modified versions starting as Mark IIA ran through to Mark IIF.

Halford had tried the various fuel mixtures during the Ricardo experiments, eventually being able to use the 'racing fuel'. As Sir Harry Ricardo describes in his book, *Memories & Machines – The Pattern of My Life*, he developed this 'racing fuel' by adding to the initial higher-octane petrol a mixture of ethyl alcohol (supplied by the Distillers Company), benzene, acetone, water plus two percent of castor oil (as upper-cylinder lubricant) and, in order to disguise the formula and prevent third-party analysis, some finely powdered bone meal which, combined with the castor oil, produced a repulsive smell. It was rated at 100-octane. This mixture when used in an existing engine, adjusted only by changing to larger carburettor jets and higher engine speeds, gave a power increase of between 5 to 10%, but with an increase in compression ratio to 8:1 a 30% power increase was possible.

In the last meeting in 1921, with the alcohol mixture Halford was second across the line in the 500cc Solo Handicap race. This was the first occasion the racing fuel was used at Brooklands. Race entrants found they had to consider using the racing fuel if they were to remain competitive. They had the choice of either Shell Racing Spirit or Discol R. (Cans were of different colour but the fuel came from the same source and marketed under an invented 'rivalry' between Shell and the Distillers).

Halford and Ricardo decided to redesign the Triumph engine to benefit

50

from the fuel now available. By the start of the 1922 season at Brooklands, the new engine was ready. It had 85mm bore and 98mm stroke and a new cylinder, with greater area of cooling fins, pent-roof cylinder head, which allowed a significant increase in valve area, with four valves operated in pairs by a dual rocker and the original push-rods and central sparking plug. After using a cast-iron cylinder head, a new head was made in a bronze alloy, obviating the need for valve seat inserts. The exhaust ports were at an angle to each other instead of parallel. The piston was a very light aluminium slipper-type and a compression ratio of 8:1. Dry-sump lubrication superseded the previous total-loss system, with a double-piston oscillating pump to provide oil to the big-ends and to scavenge the sump. Power was an estimated 25 hp at 5000 rpm. At the opening meeting of the 1922 Brooklands season, Halford entered the Triumph in the open class, competing with much larger machines, and scored an impressive win. Further successes followed and during the season various design ideas were tried and the maximum speed on record for the Triumph at Brooklands in the 1921 season was a flying-start mile at 87.80 mph.

It was decided to enter two machines in the 1922 Isle of Man TT and these were fitted with Mark IIA engines still with 80.5mm bore and 98mm stroke, a capacity of 498.8cc and compression ratio of 6.4:1. They had a Zenith H3 carburettor with 30mm choke, 150/265cc main jet, 145/270cc compensator jet and KLG Type F12 sparking plug.

Frank with Triumph "Riccy", Isle of Man TT 1922 (Patricia Draper)

The braking system on this machine was designed for normal road use and it consisted of, at the front, bicycle-type brake shoes pulled against the rim of the wheel, the shoes connected by rods each side of the wheel, the rods coupled at the top and operated by cable-connected brake lever on the handlebars. This road standard was replaced for the racing machines as described below. The rear brake, however, was a flanged steel ring clamped to the spokes of the wheel. A brake pad was pulled against the inner side of the flange by a bell-crank lever connected by rod to a foot pedal on the nearside. This braking system was quite a common practice on the early machines but, as machines of greater power become available, manufacturers began to develop the expanding-shoes drum brake. For racing purposes, particularly with the new engine, these early brake systems were quite inadequate. This did not present too great a problem on the track, but was a totally different situation when on the road at the Isle of Man TT.

Monica accompanied her husband to the island. He rode with great skill and courage and finished eleventh, but no doubt would have finished higher up the line had he not suffered a spot of tar in his eye. However, the same model Triumph was ridden by Walter Brandish and finished second. Both the Brandish and Halford machines had been fitted with a modified front brake replacing the original rim brake. This new system consisted of a grooved pulley attached to the hub of the wheel around which was fitted a cable, bound with asbestos string so that half the circumference of the pulley groove was in contact. One end of the cable anchored to the forks at the rear of the pulley and the other end extending to a handlebar brake lever. This was an improvement, but not a solution, as the heat generated caused the asbestos to carbonise and break up.

As a result of Halford's involvement in this single-cylinder engine, plus his outstanding performances on the race track, there was increasing interest in the use of overhead valves in preference to the then popular side valves. Of course, this was coupled with the Ricardo/Shell higher-octane fuel and Ricardo turbulent head, which enabled compression ratios to be raised without creating pre-ignition problems. This led to a contract from the Triumph Cycle Co to redesign their engine with compression ratio low enough for commercial fuel and with a cast-iron cylinder head. This was a very profitable deal for the Ricardo Company. Triumph continued to produce a road and a racing version until 1927. It was a very popular bike and kept Triumph in the forefront of British motorcycles.

The Vauxhall motorcycle

In 1921, the Ricardo organisation were retained as consulting engineers to a number of firms, including Vauxhall and Rolls-Royce. The Vauxhall Board were faced with the loss of the Russian market due to the Revolution plus the cessation of orders at the end of the war. At the same time, they lost the services of their skilful designer, Laurence Pomeroy, who went to work in America.

They decided to initiate a new car and engine and, shortly afterwards, a luxury motorcycle. Vauxhall commissioned Ricardo to design a high-performance three-litre engine for the car and the entire design of the motorcycle. The commission gave Ricardo a free hand to design what his experience indicated would be the best, with little commercial restraint. The car engine was used in the three Vauxhall special team cars entered in the 1922 RAC Isle of Man TT.

At this time, the Ricardo works at Shoreham on Sea was nearing completion and efforts to find accommodation for all drawing office staff was proving difficult. So it was arranged that Halford would remain in London at the Ricardo offices and Ricardo would operate from Shoreham. Ricardo has recorded that at that time he was very occupied with several ongoing projects and overseeing the completion of his new works, so he agreed to undertake the design of the three-litre engine and, as Halford was the keen motorcyclist, leave the motorcycle design to him.

It was with considerable glee that Halford settled down to undertake the design of the complete motorcycle. What emerged from the drawing board was a machine so advanced that it is only in recent years that many of the ideas incorporated are being used on modern machines. The engine was a four-cylinder in-line of 950cc capacity. Bore and stroke were both 67mm and it produced 30 hp. Engine, clutch and gearbox were a combined unit and no moving parts were visible. A shaft transmitted the drive on the nearside from the rear of the gearbox, with a universal joint at each end to a worm and wheel assembly on the rear axle. The frame was a duplex cradle of very sturdy construction. Wheels were interchangeable and were fitted with Dunlop 700x80 tyres. The machine had identical front and rear internal expanding brakes, which remained in position when the wheels were removed. It was possible to remove the cylinder head in situ and, by detaching the vertical tube connecting the saddle lug and crossbar behind the engine/gearbox unit, the gearbox and clutch could be unbolted from the engine crankcase and removed. Lighting and ignition was fed from a six-volt, seven-ampere dynamo with distributor and contact breaker. A coil and battery were located in a wooden box mounted on top of the gearbox casing and held in place by a brass strap. Top speed was around 80 mph and comfortable cruising at 50 mph was available with a fuel consumption of 70 mpg.

In view of the advanced engine design, a detailed specification is of considerable interest when related to the year in which it was designed.

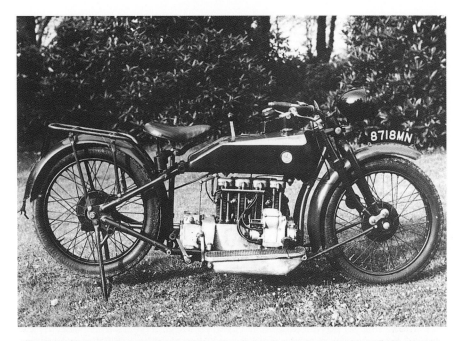

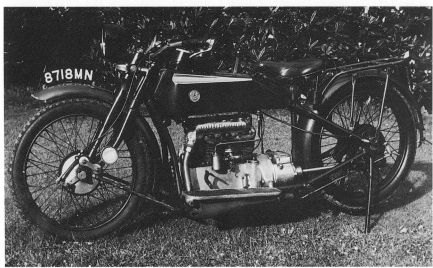

Halford-designed Vauxhall motorcycle 950cc 4-cylinder shaft drive, 1921-22 (Bob Thomas)

Individual cast-iron cylinders had integral heads and the spark plugs were screwed into the offside of the cylinders. The cylinders had a bottom flange fitted over studs protruding from the aluminium crankcase. There were two vertical valves per head, with very weak valve springs, operated by rockers (adjusted by hardened screws and lock nuts) and enclosed tappet rods. This layout, with well designed cams and the 'soft' valve springs ensured very silent valve gear. Rocker arms were fitted in plain bearings and lubricated by wick. The rocker assembly was housed in an aluminium box attached to each cylinder head by three bolts, two of which extended to fix the aluminium cover.

The connecting-rods were of H section, with plain white-metal big-end bearings and, together with a Ricardo slipper-type aluminium piston, gudgeon pins in plain bearings, each assembly weighed 20½ oz. The cast-aluminium crankcase had three main bearing housings to take a 2½-inch diameter ball race at the front and 4½-inch diameter centre and rear ball races. The crankshaft was in two sections. Lubrication was by wet sump with dippers on the big-end caps to pick up and splash oil from four troughs in a gauze tray fitted to the top of the sump, which held half a gallon of lubricant. Oil was fed to the troughs by an oil pump driven by an eccentric on the crankshaft drive gear. The drive was taken to a 6-inch diameter, multi-plate clutch (steel and bronze plates alternating) and a three-speed gearbox with two means of selection. A hand-change protruded from the centre of the divided rear of the tank and a rocker-type foot-change was fitted behind the offside foot plate. Ingenious use was made of both foot plates, the silencer being fitted underneath the nearside, and a toolbox beneath the offside. The machine was a delight to ride once the gear change was mastered.

When Halford delivered the design to Vauxhall in 1923, they made six frames and twelve engine and drive units. Two complete assemblies were made, but then the Board decided to drop the project. One complete machine was sold to a Vauxhall draughtsman for £45 and the second to an apprentice. The remaining bits and pieces became dispersed over the years. There is, however, one – and only one – of these beautiful machines still in existence and still on the road as a result of the continuing enthusiasm of Mr R A Thomas, whose efforts took twelve years from 1950. The rebuild required the manufacture of a complete frame and petrol tank, part of the front forks, handlebars and many other parts. Original drawings were obtained from Vauxhall, an essential requirement to complete such a considerable undertaking by one individual. There was a most detailed article on the machine in the 19 November 1925 issue of the Motor Cycle. Frank Halford was bitterly disappointed at the cancellation of the project. It had been an enjoyable opportunity to produce something very dear to his heart and such a project was not likely to come his way again.

By 1922, Halford had become restless, as the Ricardo Company found the direction which their market was taking meant long-range research and a predominance of industrial powerplants and this was not what he envisaged as his future. He therefore decided to leave the company and start his own consultancy, his strong desire to retain his independence reasserting itself. This did not mean the end of technical association and a few years later, in 1928, when Halford was approached by Napiers and work on designing large-power sleeve-valve aero-engines was started, he was able to consult with Ricardo and have the benefit of his experience in combustion technique. He left Ricardo having gained much experience both in design and in business matters which were to stand him in good stead in his future career.

In setting up his consultancy, his intention was to concentrate on aero-engine design, but he found it necessary to accept commissions outside aviation in order to survive. The opportunities available in the post-war slump were scarce. However, good fortune appeared in the shape of the Aircraft Disposal Company and his friend, Geoffrey de Havilland.

CHAPTER FIVE

1921 – 1934 Racing

As Frank Halford's motorcycle and motor car racing spanned thirteen years, a detailed chapter on his leisure interest has much to record. His indulgence in the sport enabled him to apply his engineering expertise and was an activity related to his major career. Apart from his participation in the 1922 Isle of Man TT, Brooklands was the venue for his racing. The first occasion he appeared at the track was at one of the few meetings held during the First World War by the British Motor-Cycle Racing Club under the auspices of the Auto Cycle Union and with permission of the authorities who were occupying the track. The category of 'cyclecars' had been added to acceptable classes to race in BMCRC events in 1913 in addition to solo and sidecar classes. On 7 August 1915, a full programme of events was held for members of the Services and was known as an 'All Khaki' meeting. Event number seven, a Passenger Half-Mile Sprint for sidecar outfits not exceeding 1000cc and cyclecars not exceeding 1100cc, attracted sixteen entrants and competitor number sixty-five was Lt F B Halford RFC driving a four-cylinder 1080cc Calthorpe Minor. Unfortunately, the results of the race are not available. This is the only recorded occasion Halford was able to race during the War.

By the time Halford returned to the UK in 1921 and took up his post with the Ricardo organisation, he was keen to start racing again and, having acquired a 500cc single-cylinder Triumph machine in racing specification, he undertook preliminary trials at the track. However, Ricardo, who was developing a new design of engine for installation in a Triumph frame, wanted Halford's help to test the machine under racing conditions and assist in its development. In 1920, Ricardo had designed, built and bench-tested a new improved 500cc engine

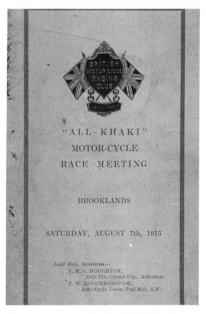

Programme cover for the "All Khaki" race meeting, Brooklands, 7 August 1915
(Brooklands Museum)

No.	Name.	Rank and Regiment.	No. of Cyl.	Machine.	Bore.	Stroke.	C.C.	Time. M.	s.	No.
51.	F. E. Barker	Cpl. A.S.C., M.T.	2	Zenith	85	85	988			51
64.	O. M. Baldwin	Cpl. A.S.C.	2	P.V.	70	85	654			64
53.	E. W. S. Bardsley	Capt. The King's Own	2	Indian	82½	93	994			53
44.	C. G. Cardew	2nd Lt. Royal Engineers	2	Zenith	70	88	654			44
13.	W. Compton-Hall	2nd Lt. Royal West Kent Regt.		Ivy Precision			500			13
65.	F. B. Halford	Lt. Royal Flying Corps	4	Calthorpe Minor	62	90	1080			65
30.	F. M. C. Houghton	2nd Lt. 25th Div. Cyclist Co.	1	Rudge Multi	85	88	499			30
46.	E. H. Kittledale	Lt. Royal Engineers		Ariel	85	88	499			46
47.	C. P. Marcel	Asst. Paymaster R.N.R.	2	Indian	82½	93	994			47
66.	W. G. McMinnies	C.P.O., R.N.A.S.	2	Morgan Cyclecar			1100			66
67.	B. J. Moore	Mechanic Royal Flying Corps	4	Richmond Car	65	115	1065			67
68.	W. S. Pellew	2nd Lt. A.S.C., M.T.	4	Baby Peugeot	55	90	856			68
23.	H. W. Tait	Lt. D.L.I.								23
69.	C. R. Taylor	Lt. R.G.A.		Singer-Lt. Car						69
74.	R. G. Thomas			G.N.						74
75.	H. F. Edwards	Pte. Artists Rifles	2	Zenith	90	77½	994			75

No.	Name.	Rank and Regiment.	No. of Cyl.	Machine.	Bore.	Stroke.	C.C.	Time. M.	s.	No.
70.	F. E. Barker	Cpl. A.S.C., M.T.	2	Zenith	60	60	349			70
5.	J. Alcock	Flight Warrant Officer R.N.A.S.	2	Douglas	60.5	60	349			5
6.	G. L. Andrew	Capt. Army Cyclist Corps	2	Douglas	60.5	60	349			6
7.	P. T. Chevallier	Capt. 13th Middlesex Regt.	2	Douglas	60.5	60	349			7
2.	C. H. Dimmock	2nd Lt. 9th Loyal N. Lancs. Regt.	1	Connaught			270			2
8.	L. A. Fedden	Pte. A.S.C.	2	Douglas	60.5	60	349			8
9.	Maurice Newnham	1st Class Air Mechanic R.F.C.	2	Douglas	60.5	60	349			9
39.	W. Stevens	Cpl. Royal Engineers	1	A.J.S.	74	81	349			39
4.	A. Ward	Cpl. Royal Fusiliers		New Hudson						4

Entrants for Event 7 with Halford listed under No 65   (Brooklands Museum)

and, having fitted it into a Triumph frame, had George Shemans test it at Brooklands for over 100 laps at speeds from 65 to 79 mph. This machine came to be known as the Triumph 'Riccy'. Halford expended considerable time on the track testing performance and, in conjunction with Ricardo, making many modifications. Steady progress was made and a reliable engine was available as a prototype producing 20 bhp at 4000 rpm. It was decided that the development had reached a stage when the machine could be entered in a race.

On 2 July 1921, the 500 mile race was held at Brooklands with a total of 64 starters from all classes who lined up at 7.00am for this popular event. To assist in identifying the classes for both timekeepers and spectators, riders wore coloured jackets: White – 250cc Class A, Blue – 350cc Class B, Yellow – 500cc Class C, Green – 750cc Class D, Red – 1000cc Class E. Shemans was entered in Class C on the Triumph 'Riccy' and finished third, being beaten by V E Horsman on a Norton who averaged 63.65 mph and by F Edwards on a standard Triumph at 59.34 mph. Ricardo entered 'Riccy' in a number of events at the track during the year for Halford to ride. It was during 1921 that alcohol fuels came into increasing use and, as a result, higher speeds were constantly achieved. These fuels continued to be used throughout the season. The 1921 'Riccy' effort is summarised as follows:-

27 July	BMCRC 4th Meeting 3 lap 500cc Solo Scratch Race – third place
24 Aug	Record attempts – see Auto Cycle Union Records listed below
27 Aug	BMCRC 5th Meeting 500cc Solo Handicap 3 lap Race – Halford finished but not placed
8 Oct	BMCRC Championship Races, 5 laps – Third place
5 Nov	BMCRC last meeting of the season 500cc Solo Handicap 3 laps – again, Halford finished third

On 24 August and 17 November, there were various end of season record attempts during which Halford captured four Class C records and two Class D records. The Auto Cycle Union Record Book for 1921 lists Halford's record successes. The data was verified by A V Ebblewhite, the official timekeeper, as follows:-

F B Halford, Brooklands, Triumph 80.5mm bore, 98mm stroke – mean speeds

17.11.21	Class C 500cc Flying-Start Mile	87.80 mph
24.08.21	Class C 500cc Flying-Start Mile	83.91 mph
17.11.21	Class C 500cc Flying-Start Mile	81.78 mph
24.08.21	Class C 500cc Standing-Start Ten Mile	76.01 mph
17.11.21	Class C 500cc Standing-Start Ten Mile	80.09 mph
24.08.21	Class C 500cc Fifty Mile	77.27 mph
24.08.21	Class C 500cc One Hour	76.74 mph
24.08.21	Class D 750cc Flying-Start Five Mile	76.72 mph
24.08.21	Class D 750cc Flying-Start Ten Mile	76.01 mph

It was a remarkably good effort with the 'Riccy' on top form to round off a successful season with the initial four-valve engine. Ricardo and Halford could be well satisfied with their 1921 results which showed the engine to be reliable and powerful. The following year, with Halford's involvement, the engine was much modified – as described in Chapter Four. The BMCRC Brooklands season opened on 8 April and George Dance with a new very fast Sunbeam won the 350cc 3-lap event and entered the same machine in the 3-lap Solo Scratch race for machines of 350cc up to 500cc finishing second. Halford ran in this event but was unplaced. The Sunbeams set the speed targets for the season.

On 6 May, the BMCRC held their Brooklands Senior Tourist Trophy Meeting. Four races were held for 250cc, 350cc, 500cc and 1000cc machines. Each race was over a distance of 81.5 miles (30 laps) starting at the Fork. Halford finished second in the 500cc race, averaging 68.89 mph.

Frank and Monica at the pits, Isle of Man TT, June 1922 (Patricia Draper)

He found he was battling with some very experienced riders. The leading exponents during this period at the track were Victor Horsman, Rex Judd and George Tucker – all riding Nortons, Jack Emerson and Cyril Pullin both with Douglases, C P Wood on the two-stroke Scott and Bert Le Vack with a New Imperial/JAP.

In a hot summer in June, Halford with Monica went to the Isle of Man where they stayed at the Prince of Wales Hotel, Ramsey, for the TT. Monica wrote to her mother that Frank was suffering from a poisoned eye caused by a spot of tar during practice, but was going to race. A total of 67 entrants was listed. Ricardo and Halford had entered four machines, prepared for the Senior TT and supported by adequate spares and the

Cornering in the 1922 TT (Brooklands Museum)

60

services of a Ricardo engineer, A Doughty. The other riders were Walter Brandish, Fred Edmonds and Reuben Harveyson. Edmonds came off his machine at Union Mills on the second lap and broke a handlebar. Harveyson retired on the third lap with a stuck valve. With the redesigned engine going very well, Halford felt confident of getting a good race. He completed the course, finishing eleventh. However, Triumph were very pleased as Walter Brandish finished second on a similar-powered machine.

The 10 June at Brooklands and Halford was on the Triumph for the two-lap Solo Handicap, unplaced behind a Norton win. As part of Ricardo's contract with Triumph he had agreed to regain the 500cc One Hour record before the annual Olympia show opened. Some ten days before the opening date, Halford had successfully lapped Brooklands at 68 mph, then the weather changed for the worse. On the day before the show opened, it was still raining heavily and time was running out. At 5.00pm, he had to start the attempt. The daylight was fading. Goggles were useless. He continued to lap, later with the aid of cars lighting the Fork and finishing straight with their headlights and after the most painful hour's riding he succeeded. The Triumph stand flew its banner the next day.

In July of 1922, the track authorities were under pressure from local residents who objected to the noise, in particular that created by the motorcycles. In an effort to placate the protesters, the Clerk of the Course, Colonel F Lindsay Lloyd, issued a notice that all vehicles using the track must be adequately silenced, or would be banned from the entire estate. This was the birth of the Brooklands silencer for the motorcycles. July 8 saw the Motor Cycle Club Summer Meeting and, in the Class C 3-lap Solo Scratch Race with the start and finish at the fork, Halford riding the Triumph 'Riccy' finished third. This was followed on the 15th of the month with two races, the 100-mile Giant Handicap and a 3-lap Solo Handicap. There is no record of his placing available.

In August, the 500-mile race was cancelled due to the track authorities' sensitivity over the noise issue much to the fury of the motorcycle fraternity. September and October were months for a great deal of record attempts for most of the classes for both solo and sidecar. New records were set, but this time the Triumph 'Riccy' was not an entrant. On 21 October at the BMCRC Championship Meeting, Halford took part in the 500cc solo 3-lap race again riding the 'Riccy' and finished third. The BARC held a Remembrance Day Motor Race Meeting at Brooklands on 11 November. The programme included a number of events for motorcycles as well as cars. The fifth race at 3.10pm was the Weybridge 90 mph 3-lap Handicap for motorcycles of any class. Of the 28 entrants, Halford was No 11 on his 500cc Triumph with a handicap of 30 seconds. He finished but was not placed. On 23, 24 and 25 November, a spate of successful record attempts were made on these last days of the season, but Halford did not compete in record attempts this year.

At the re-opening of the track following winter closure, it was announced that motorcycle speeds would, from now on, be measured on the 50ft median line of the track instead of the 10ft median line previously used. This was an attempt to remove the anomalies between calculated and actual times. Halford entered in only two meetings in 1923, the BMCRC 7 April 3-lap Handicap and the 3-lap Scratch Race. No winning success. His last appearance on two wheels was on 5 May in the Brooklands Senior Century for 500cc machines over 100 miles; again the final results are unrecorded. He now intended to further his race career by changing to four wheels and, in April, became a member of the Junior Car Club. The era of the Halford Special was to start twelve months later.

In 1923, Halford became associated with the Bamber & Martin Company, then producing a small number of Lionel Martin's cars to order. To alleviate some of the company's financial difficulties, he provided two loans of £1,000 each in January and February. In view of the Company's dire straits two years later, when they went into receivership having built only 62 cars from 1920 to 1925, it is not known whether Halford's loans were repaid. However, in 1923, Halford was invited to drive for Lionel Martin, so joining the small band of loyal Aston Martin owners and amateur racers, which included George Eyston, W G Barlow, J C Douglas and R C Morgan. Their efforts on track and in speed and hill climb events greatly helped to expand the race programme and provide valuable publicity for the Marque.

The first recorded race meeting at Brooklands in which Halford participated driving an Aston Martin was the JCC Members Spring Meeting on 28 April 1923. He was allocated the 1921 1½-litre 'Bunny' into which he had the twin overhead cam Grand Prix engine fitted. He entered six of the eleven events.

Event No 2	Junior Short Handicap 5½ miles for cars and cyclecars up to 1500cc. Finished but not placed.
Event No 4	Scratch Sprint ½ mile. Finished, not placed.
Event No 6	Junior Long Handicap 8½ miles. Halford's handicap 30 seconds. Finished, not placed.
Event No 8	1½ litre Sealed Handicap 8½ miles, which he won with P du Cane (Bugatti) second and J C Douglas (Aston Martin) third.
Event No 10	Grand 10 lap Handicap. He had a 1m 40s handicap and finished unplaced.
Event No 11	Spring Sweepstake Handicap. He was on pole position for the start with zero handicap but did not finish in the first three.

It was a good day of racing, logging experience of the track with four wheels instead of two and the chance to size-up the opposition for future competition.

At the Whitsun meeting, Halford drove a twin-cam Aston Martin (this was probably the 1922 200-mile race car) entered by Lionel Martin, in the fourth race – the 75 mph Short Handicap Race of 5.75 miles and lapped at a creditable 87.22 mph and won; following this, the eighth race – the 90 mph Long Handicap (he had a 52-second handicap) and the ninth race – the 75 mph Long Handicap (this time a 14-second handicap). He finished each race but unsuccessfully, not being in the first three. His next appearance was on 2 June in the Essex MC's Essex Senior (100 mph) Short Handicap, a 26 second handicap resulted in not finishing in the first three. The 23 June was the JCC 90 mph Short Handicap and the Green Aston Martin had a 9-second handicap. Two more races, the 100 mph Long Handicap and the 90 mph Long Handicap – again resulted in no place finishes. However, the next day on the 24th, representing Lionel Martin, he took the record for the Test Hill in 9.14 seconds – 26.27 mph with 'Bunny'. At the BARC August Bank

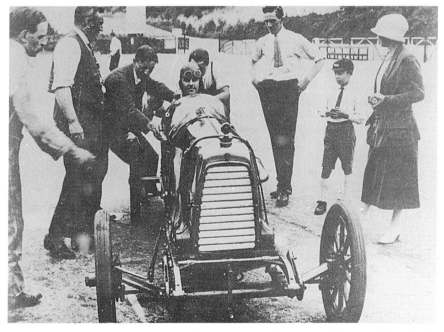

Halford in the cockpit of the Aston Martin "Razorblade". Lionel Martin is second from left.
(A B Demaus)

63

Holiday Meeting, he won the 100 mph Short Handicap but was unplaced in the 75 mph Long Handicap. On 14 August, Halford piloted the twin-cam, sixteen-valve Aston Martin in the Light Car Class Standing Start Half Mile and took the mile and kilometre record at 74.12 mph.

For the Brooklands Midsummer Meeting of 1923, Lionel Martin produced a remarkable special Aston Martin. This had a two-litre, twin overhead cam engine which had previously been fitted in the car owned then by George Eyston. The Special was fitted with a single-seat body 18½ inches wide on a very narrow chassis, with a front track of 4 feet and a rear track of only 3 feet. It had a solid back axle fitted with small brakes, there being no front wheel brakes (as was often the case at that time). The streamlined body was built by the de Havilland Aircraft Company and the intention was to take the Light Car Hour record which stood at 101.39 miles. It was known as 'Razorblade'. Sammy Davis had tried it out at Brooklands with the repeated result of it discarding its offside front tyre when leaving the Members Banking at high speed. Lionel Martin asked Halford to drive it in the 90 mph Short Handicap Race. It performed very well, lapping at 98.04 mph, but further development was needed. However, it won the 100 mph Short Handicap at 98.81 mph with Halford at the wheel. Sadly, it never achieved its goal of reaching the One Hour record.

Following Halford's debut with 'Razorblade', he had regular availability to use 'Bunny'. This car had been extensively raced with considerable success by a selection of drivers, including Lionel Martin, E R Hall, Clive Gallop, Kensington Moir, Sammy Davis (Brooklands Long Distance Record, May 1922) and Bertie S Marshall (Le Mans Sept 1921 – not the 24-hour race). Completing the Brooklands season with considerable track experience gained, he had also joined Lionel Martin in hill climbs and speed events and, on 12 May, piloting 'Bunny' he had a 1st and 2nd at the Aston Hill climb, followed at the end of the month at Skegness with Martin on his first car, AM 270, and Halford on 'Bunny' they finished with three 1sts and three 2nds. At the end of June at Porthcawl Springs and Caerphilly Hill climb, Martin and Halford collected 1sts and 2nds. September took him to Aston Hill, again with the same car with the 16-valve engine, and was fastest in class.

He suspended his racing career in order to complete the design of the engine for his Special. As soon as the detailed drawing were complete, orders were placed for manufacture. He incorporated into this design his accumulated experience built up since 1914 and the result showed many features which were to become accepted as the future direction for racing car engines. This powerplant, a supercharged six-cylinder of one-and-a-half litres capacity was based on a deep light-alloy casting into which the six steel cylinder liners fitted with rubber seals at the base were in contact with the

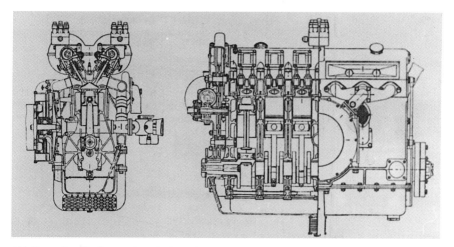

1½-litre, 6-cylinder engine designed by Halford for his Special   (Author)

coolant. The bore and stroke were 63mm x 83mm. The crankshaft ran in seven plain bearings and, for the first time, connecting rods were of 'Y' alloy (4% copper, 2% nickel, 1.5% magnesium, the balance aluminium), the gudgeon pins being fitted direct into the rods without bearing inserts. Both connecting rods and pistons were forged and each assembly of rod, piston and piston rings weighed under one pound. Big-end bearings were bronze lined with white metal. The cast-iron cylinder head had a metal-to-metal lapped joint with no gasket. Twelve inclined valves were operated by finger-type rockers from two camshafts driven by a train of spur gears at the rear of the engine. Two 12mm spark plugs per cylinder were energised by twin BTH magnetos driven from the camshaft train and mounted at the rear, to be accessible from the cockpit side of the bulkhead. These replaced the original distributors mounted midway on top of the camshaft covers and driven from the centre of the camshafts. The engine was initially boosted by an exhaust-driven turbo-blower. This was indeed a most advanced idea in the twenties. The carburrettor was attached to the flange of a pipe which passed through the centre of the crankcase and fed the mixture into the centrifugal blower, the outlet of which was connected to an inter-cooler beneath the sump, thence back to the other side, piped to the inlet manifold.

It was the first car to be fitted with a turbo-blower and it would be another fifty years before a production car had a turbo-blower and another ten years before the turbo-charge GP formula came into racing. Halford found this form of supercharging did not give the expected power increase and he discarded it in favour of a Roots-type supercharger fitted in front of the radiator and driven by a universal-jointed shaft from the front of the crankshaft. The engine produced 96 bhp at 5500 rpm. The probable reason why he discarded the exhaust-driven blower after initial testing was because it was found that the back pressure in the exhaust system was somewhat more than the pressure produced by the blower. Such a design of turbo-blower would be of value when fitted to an aero-engine as, at altitude, the pressure difference across the turbine would increase giving greater speed to the turbine and increasing the pressure rise through the blower.

In 1924, Halford acquired the ex W G Barlow car (OR-1) from George Eyston who had taken it to Boulogne to race in the Small Car Race and had a disastrous meeting with a telegraph pole. Halford did no racing in the first eight months of 1924 as, during such time as his design practice allowed, he wanted to concentrate on designing and building his Special.

His next appearance on the racing scene was on 20 September when he was the driver of Alvis No 2, one of the new 4-cylinder 1½-litre Alvis entered by T G John in the popular JCC 200 Mile Race at the Brooklands track. With 20 starters in the 1500cc Class and a total of 47 entrants, classes were colour-coded by painting the bonnets. Both Alvis were new cars, being specials developed by Alvis following their 1923 success. The race was won by the Darracq team finishing 1, 2 and 3 with Halford coming in 4th.

It was not until the BARC August Bank Holiday Meeting in 1925 that Halford appeared as an entrant introducing his new A M Halford Special.

W G Barlow with his 1923 short chassis GP replica Aston Martin from which Halford used the chassis for his AM Special   (Author)

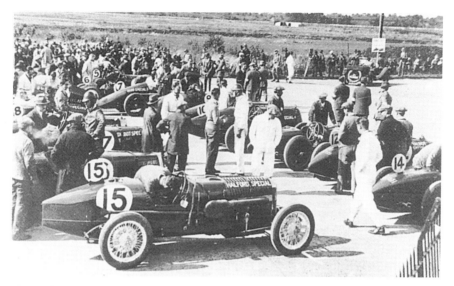

The Halford Special – No 15 at the start of the JCC 200-miles race, September 1926
(Brooklands Museum)

The car was fitted with a most attractive two-seat streamlined body, finished in white with ultramarine chassis and wheels. He entered for only one race (the 2nd) in the programme; this was the 100 mph Short Handicap. The car ran well but was unplaced at the finish.

He was particularly keen to run his new car in the prestigious JCC '200' to be held on 26 September. On the Tuesday before the race, Halford took the car round on practice laps allowing the handicappers to make their assessment of this new machine. On the 26th, two rows of entrants were lined up across the fork and each car had a number displayed on a vertical disc above the tail. The A M Halford was No 9. All cars carried a mechanic alongside the driver. By the end of the first lap, Halford was lying in eighth place and the pace was blisteringly fast. Seagrave, who was in the lead, completed his 20th lap whilst the A M Halford was still on its 17th. However, by half distance, Halford had moved up to third place but on the 50th lap disaster struck. The engine overheated due to loss of water and Halford and his mechanic had to push the car into the pits, then had to wait until the engine was cool enough to allow them to replenish the coolant. They restarted, only to run out of petrol after a short distance, resulting in another push into the pits from the far side of the track. A shower of rain followed by some sleet enlivened the proceedings. The result was a win for Seagrave followed by Masetti (both driving Darracqs), Johnstone (Fraser-

FBH racing the Special – Brooklands 1926   (Brooklands Museum)

Nash) and Halford, who had raced through the field to finish 4th in class and 9th overall, having averaged 61.80 mph.

The BARC Meeting on 12 September saw the Special in the 90 mph Short Handicap (15 secs), the 100 mph Long Handicap (46 secs) and the 90 mph Long Handicap (16 secs); finishing in all three but not in the first three. His last race of the year was at the Essex MC Brooklands Meeting on 3 October as an entrant in the Essex 50 Mile Handicap (a minimum of nineteen laps was required). A handicap of 2 mins 18 secs put his start fifth out of sixteen. The result is not available.

Development continued during the car's racing programme and, at the end of the year, a new engine was installed which gave 120 bhp at 5500 rpm supercharged at 11 lb per sq in using the Roots-type supercharger. This engine was built by Hamilton Gordon of the Weyburn Engineering Co. As the original small Aston Martin radiator had now been replaced by one of greater capacity, the AM initials in the name were discarded and henceforth it was entered as the Halford Special.

Three races were entered in the BARC Easter Meeting starting his 1926 season. The fourth race – the 90 mph Short Handicap of 5.75 miles, the sixth race – the 90 mph Long Handicap of 8.5 miles and the seventh race – the 100 mph Long Handicap of 8.5 miles added to his racing mileage but not to his success.

At the BARC Whitsun Meeting in May 1926, Halford took the Special to victory in the 90 mph Short Handicap at an average speed of 95.86 mph and achieved his fastest lap at 104.63 mph. The Surbiton MC Meeting on 24 May followed and he won the 90 mph Short Handicap and was third in the 90 mph Long Handicap finishing a good day's racing with a second in the 100 mph Long Handicap.

Following this success, the BARC Summer Meeting saw a great duel in the 1½-litre class with Malcolm Campbell whose four-cylinder Talbot put in a fastest lap at 109.94 mph, which just beat Halford's 109.22 mph. Halford went on to finish the distance but was not in the first four. Next, at the same meeting, came the 100 mph Long Handicap and the Special got round at 109.94

Returning from the JCC 200 in which FBH came tenth overall   (Author)

mph and won at an average of 102.04 mph. Continuing a very full day of racing, Halford started in the 90 mph 3-lap Long Handicap after being re-handicapped by eight seconds. He made the fastest standing start lap of 94.5 mph and the two remaining laps at 109.70 mph finishing second behind Parry Thomas in a Lanchester.

The RAC Grand Prix followed in August. Prior to World War II, there were only four Grand Prix races held in Britain – at Brooklands in 1926 and 1927 and at Donington in 1937 and 1938. These were not entitled British Grand Prix. The 1926 race was limited to 1½-litre cars and over a distance of 290 miles. Halford got away well and he continued holding fourth place until, on the 83rd lap, the universal joint failed. The BARC Meeting on 11 September, as a warm-up for the coming '200', the Special appeared in the Lightning Short Handicap and the 100 mph Long Handicap just finishing outside the first three. He returned in September for the JCC 200 miles race in which he came sixth in class and tenth overall. This was a good result in the circumstances as a constant-mesh gear failed in the gearbox just after the start and he continued in top gear only.

This ended the 1926 season and also his regular racing in the Special. In 1927, George Eyston bought the car and continued to race it throughout the season at Brooklands, but his best result was a fifth place in the 1927 French Grand Prix at Montlhery. After this, he sold the car because *"it was not fast*

Halford in the Roots supercharged Halford Special, Brooklands 1933 (Author)

enough", although in Halford's hands during the previous year, the car consistently lapped the Brooklands outer circuit at between 100 to 110 mph. Halford was now increasingly involved with his aero-engine design consultancy and unable to spare the time, or the increasing cost, to continue a satisfactory racing programme. His name does re-appear in July 1933 when he took the Special up the Test Hill at a record 26.27 mph in 19.14 seconds. Then, in 1934, he was part of a team in the Light Car Club Relay Race at Brooklands, driving a four-cylinder GN.

In later years, the design of the Special's engine was simplified for production purposes and made submersible for use in lifeboats; the first being fitted to the Eastbourne lifeboat. It continued to be supplied for this purpose for many years. Halford's racing career at Brooklands between the years 1922 to 1926 was indeed reasonably successful, but he was never as well known to the public as his contemporaries Malcolm Campbell, George Eyston, John Cobb and Parry Thomas. However, within the membership of the BARC, he was a much respected figure. Fellow drivers had great respect for his combination of engineering abilities and driving skills. It is pleasing to know that the Halford Special is still in existence thanks to the devoted efforts over a number of years by the great enthusiast, James Cheyne and is currently in the Brooklands Museum.

It would be useful, at this point, to clarify any confusion which may have arisen from there being two Major Halfords who participated in motor-

FBH returns to Brooklands paddock with the Special   (Brooklands Museum)

racing at the track. They were not related. Major Edward Aphelstan Halford is on record as driving a GN light car at the Light Car Club meetings at Brooklands. Firstly on 16 July 1932 then on 22 July 1933 and 21 July 1934. All were LCC meetings. He next appeared in 1936 and 1937 with his Halford Cross Rotary Special. This was a single-seater HRG racer powered by a 1½-litre Meadows engine to which he had fitted a Cross rotary-valve cylinder head in place of the standard OHV head. He entered for one meeting on 27 June 1936 followed by three races in 1937 on 27 February, 17 May and 10 July. Unfortunately, he did not achieve any great success in return for his efforts to pioneer a different design of valve system. E A Halford financed, and was part designer, of the HRG being the 'H' with Robbins of Trogans, the 'R', and Godfrey from GN, the 'G'.

There was a curiously parallel history between the two Halfords. They both attended Felsted School – E A H being two years after F B H – and both joined the Royal Flying Corps – F B H in 1914 and E A H in 1915. Both attaining the rank of major. It is not surprising that their records became confused in later years.

FBH at Airdisco, Croyden 1926   (Author)

CHAPTER SIX

1923 – 1928 The consultancy and Aircraft Disposal Company

On leaving the Ricardo Company, Halford set up his consultancy in a very small office in an attic in Ladbrook Grove in North Kensington, London. The rent was five shillings and six pence per week and the year was 1923. He engaged the first member of his staff, John L P Brodie, in November. He had first met Brodie in the drawing office of Arrol Johnston when involved in the development of the BHP engine and was most impressed by him. John Brodie was to become a close friend and remained as Halford's right-hand man for over 32 years.

Now that Halford was his own master, he set to work to make use of the extensive experience he had gained over the last nine years, which put him in a unique position to create aero power units to meet the needs of the civil aviation industry, which was picking itself up after the intensive effort of the war years, followed by the almost complete shut down immediately the war finished. At 29 years of age, he planned to see the fulfilment of his driving enthusiasm and ambition to be at the top of the heap when the aircraft industry gathered pace.

During the war, the manufacturing side of the engineering industry had learnt swiftly to produce complex items with great accuracy on a production basis. The industry which emerged from the war years had developed at a speed unpremeditated in 1913. There were now workshops equipped with machine tools of far greater sophistication than a decade earlier and what was equally important, designers, technicians and skilled artisans were available in greater numbers. They were in a position to handle the complexities which were to come forward in the post-war era with the emergence of civil aircraft construction and airline-operating industries.

Halford believed that the way forward in aero-engine design was small-bore cylinders, bore stroke ratios approaching 1/1, with higher piston speeds and crankshaft speeds in the 2000 to 2500 rpm range. In 1923, as part of this development and at the same time indulging his enjoyment of racing, he started a design for a 1½-litre six-cylinder supercharged engine for a racing car. What emerged was, as in the case of his Vauxhall motorcycle design, something way ahead of its time. Details of this car engine are described in Chapter Five.

In 1924, he was invited to act as consultant to the Aircraft Disposal Company at Waddon, Croydon. This company, known as Airdisco, was registered in 1920 and was responsible for the purchase of almost the entire stock of surplus aircraft engines in the country following the cessation of the

The Renault 8-cylinder 80bhp

war. It has been said that this amounted to 30,000 units. The consultancy role would be to assess in what form and context these surplus engines could be marketed. He accepted the offer and an office and test facilities were made available for his use at the Airdisco factory.

Following a review of the engines available and a discussion with the Airdisco directors, he selected the 80 hp eight-cylinder-vee Renault as the first project, knowing there was a possible market with de Havilland for the DH51 three-seater biplane. The existing cylinder head and valve gear were discarded and a new design of head in aluminium with overhead valves substituted. The engine was re-rated at 144 bhp and marketed as the 'Airdisco'. Its installation in the DH51 proved successful.

Following this initial effort, other engines came under scrutiny and were the subject of the 'Halford treatment' of a design review including the Wolseley Viper, 300 hp Fiat and the Sunbeam Nubian, Zulu, Amazon and Afridi. Unfortunately, none of these redesigns found a market.

During this time, Geoffrey de Havilland started on his plans to produce a range of light aircraft to encourage private flying. There was a potential market waiting for suitable machines, at a price affordable to individuals and, more importantly, to stimulate the growth of flying clubs in this country, who needed a safe, easy-to-fly and easy-to-maintain machine which could become the 'standard' aircraft for clubs. To this end, de Havilland produced the drawings for the DH60 Moth, which would be a two-seat open cockpit biplane two-thirds the size of the DH51, thus requiring a smaller powered engine than the Airdisco. As de Havilland realised, it would be necessary to have this aircraft on the market by 1925 in order to be ahead of his rivals. He could find no suitable existing engine available and turned again to Halford, who was keen to design a new unit to fulfil the requirement. But, in considering the time needed to design, build a prototype, test and obtain certification, de Havilland realised this course would jeopardise his market and something must be done to overcome the delay. Both he and Halford reviewed their options and, concentrating on the vast quantity of Airdisco stock and of the many engines available, they decided to make use of as much of the 80 hp Renault parts as possible. Having already modified the Renault into the 140 horsepower Airdisco, Halford believed he could produce a four-cylinder engine of half the Airdisco output.

To start on this idea, both Halford and de Havilland laid out the actual components of the Renault on a bench and from that basis selected four pistons, connecting-rods, a single bank of four cylinders, a gear train which, with a new cast crankcase and five-bearing crankshaft, would be the new engine of 4.5-litres capacity and weighing 286 lb. This was only arrived at after prolonged discussion and various layouts with related calculations were explored. One important consideration was the economics and the fact that an unused Renault engine could be bought for 25 shillings (125 pence in today's money) brought the scales down in favour of making maximum use of the surplus engines.

de Havilland realised that he was stretched financially and would not be able to support the cost of development and testing this new engine. He set out to persuade the Airdisco directors to accept these costs on the grounds that it would create a market for the sale of their war surplus. In this he was successful and the four-cylinder was designed, built and tested in two months and rated at 64 bhp at 1800 rpm with a maximum output of 68 bhp at 2000 rpm. The engine was named 'Cirrus' and became the engine for the DH60 Moth which first flew in February 1925. This light plane was so successful it became the parent of a series of light aircraft used world-wide.

Before continuing the story of the de Havilland/Halford co-operation, the consultancy was required to look at an old and familiar engine, the Puma, which will be remembered as the Siddeley-made modified BHP. A large quantity were sold to the new Russian Air Force and consideration was given to up-rating it. The result was an increased capacity from 18.85 to 20.70 litres and a 200 rpm increase to 1600 rpm which gave a 335 bhp output for a weight of 665 lb. Because of the power increase, a stiffer crankshaft had to be used. By good fortune, the crankshaft of the Atlantic could be easily adapted. The result was the Nimbus. Installed in DH9s, it proved highly successful and reliable and was used for aerial survey work in Africa,

Australia and South America. These surveys were carried out by the Aircraft Operating Company and one of these aircraft covered 1½ million miles without problems.

The success of the Cirrus I in the DH Moth resulted in a demand for more power and the Cirrus II was the result. This was a modification of the Cirrus I with re-designed cylinders of 110mm bore, increasing the capacity to 4.94 litres. The cylinder head was fitted with bronze valve seats, an improved valve gear and carburation, forged aluminium-alloy connecting-rods and gave 80 bhp at 1800 rpm with 85 bhp as maximum power for take-off. All this was accomplished during 1925.

In 1926, a further engine – the 95 hp Cirrus III – came out. By this time, the Aircraft Disposal Company was coming to the end of its trading and the Cirrus series was continued and manufactured by the Hermes Engine Company and sold as the Cirrus Hermes having been further refined to give 105 bhp. The next engine to continue the series was the Hermes II of 115 bhp and was the first inverted engine in the range. Hermes III and IV of 120 and 140 bhp were produced over the next few years. In 1934, the Hermes Engine Company was bought by the Blackburn Aircraft Company at Brough. In that year, the prototype Cirrus Minor of 3.605 litres, 80 to 90 bhp at 2600 rpm was tested.

In September 1926, Halford was the subject of an article by the editor of

Halford in the Special outside Airdisco Works, 1926   (Patricia Draper)

Motor Sport under their Motoring Sportsman series inspired by his successes with the Halford Special. At the time of the interview, held at the Airdisco offices, it is reported he was in the midst of recording the results of seven days continuous bench testing of the Cirrus II engine. At the end of 1926, Halford's association with Airdisco came to an end and, with Brodie, he continued with other work in the North Kensington offices. A goodly amount of time was spent on design modifications to the Halford Special car.

A new opportunity arose from a proposal by Geoffrey de Havilland, which would require an increase in staff and a move to larger premises. This was found at Windsor House, Victoria Street, London. (Windsor House no longer exists, being demolished in the redevelopment of Victoria Street after World War II).

The de Havilland Aircraft Company, realising they could not expect the supply of engines built from surplus parts to continue for much longer, decided to undertake the manufacture of engines in their own factory. Also, under the existing arrangement, the supply of engines was outside their control, which could create problems in meeting their customers' orders for aircraft. A new extension to the works at the Stag Lane aerodrome site was put in hand and discussions with Halford to provide an engine design service specifically for de Havilland were finalised, so the requirement to engage design staff for the consultancy became a matter of urgency. The second member of the staff to be engaged was W H Arscott as a designer, followed by Basil Williams, an ex-Airdisco employee, who was responsible for the drawing schedules and the modification procedures. In November 1927, a fourth member joined the small team. This was Eric Moult, a design man with experience in metallurgy who had previously been involved in the setting up of the firm which became High Duty Alloys. Dr Moult became technical assistant to Halford. Another addition, also from Airdisco, was Miss Allen, to do the tracing. In the present days of computer design and print-out, the creation of drawings suitable for production is highly specialised and no longer requires the tedious processes of yesteryear. An original pencil drawing on semi-transparent paper could be blueprint copied but it was easily damaged or torn so, when completed, checked and approved, it was the tracer's job to make an accurate tracing using Indian ink on a wax-coated linen sheet. This provided a robust and more easily reproduced basis for blueprinting. It was about this time that Miss E MacDonald joined to become Halford's secretary, an appointment which continued for many years. John Brodie now acted as manager and chief draughtsman, leaving Halford free to concentrate on the design basis and the business side.

As the consultancy was an independent organisation and provided a design service, an acceptable means of remuneration for those services had to be devised. This resulted in payment being made under a number of service headings:

First   A consultancy fee paid for a specific design.
Second A payment for each blue print issued graded on size of drawing.
Third   A royalty per engine in production, subject to it meeting an approved power output.

The Cirrus-powered Moth had galvanised the creation of flying clubs in the UK and a more powerful unit was needed. The first DH engine, which started the series known as the Gipsy engines, came into existence in 1927, designed for installation in the DH71 – a small racing monoplane – built to be flown by the chief test pilot, Hubert Broad. The power unit gave 135 bhp at 2850 rpm. The aircraft was very successful and broke the 100 kilometre record at 186 mph. The engine, which then went into production in 1928 as the Gipsy I, was a detuned version of the racing unit and powered the DH60, Gipsy Moth.

This engine, being designed without the restraints imposed by having to use parts from other existing engines, took the form of an upright, in-line, air-cooled four-cylinder unit of 5.23 litres. It had cast-iron cylinders with aluminium-alloy cylinder heads fitted with vertical valves (instead of inclined), a compression ratio reduced to 5:1 from 5.5:1. It used a five-bearing crankshaft in an aluminium-alloy crankcase and the propeller was changed to left-hand tractor to avoid the slipstream blowing the exhaust gases into the cockpit.

As the design organisation got into its stride, both Halford and Brodie operated a system of controlling standards with careful detailed checking of drawings by both of them, before any drawing was issued to de Havilland. As a result, there were no complaints from the customer that parts did not fit or that tolerances were unsuitable when the Works started production. Another excellent arrangement was the weekly meeting at Stag Lane attended by a strong DH management representation, plus Halford and Brodie as the design representation. The fact that there was a good exchange of views and that any potential problems were addressed early contributed to a smoother relationship and reduced the risk of production delays.

De Havilland planned to design an enlarged version of the little DH71 as an interceptor fighter aircraft to be powered by an engine which would have the power output of four Gipsy Is. To meet this challenge, Halford produced the 'H' layout of cylinders, an arrangement of four banks of cylinders with two crankshafts geared to a single propeller shaft. The design work was carried out at Victoria Street but, on the instructions of the Air Ministry, the drawings were passed to Napiers who had the production capacity. This engine emerged as the Rapier. Halford's Napier work is covered in Chapter Eight.

In 1927, Halford was elected a Fellow of the Royal Aeronautical Society. In the following year, 1928, Halford increased the number of staff to cope with the Napier and DH work now being carried out. This meant that a further move to larger premises had to be considered and was accomplished in early 1929. Other work came into the office at that time, one of which was the design of the Austin Hayes automatic transmission gear with overdrive for the 18 hp Austin car.

The Austin Hayes automatic transmission

This attempt to produce a car transmission system to provide an automatic drive with infinitely-variable ratios was one of a number of similar ideas which emerged at that time. Halford was required to develop the idea into a practical design and produce the drawings from which the unit could be manufactured. The illustration shows the basic principal and a description of its operation follows.

The unit consists of a disc, one side of which has a continuous groove of semi-circular section, this disc being attached to the output shaft of the clutch. Facing this, a similar disc – also grooved and attached to a shaft connected to the propeller shaft. The grooved faces of the discs face each other and between them is inserted six evenly-spaced rollers which transmit the drive by frictional contact obtained by pressing the two discs together. The speeds of the discs are varied one to the other by adjusting the flat rollers so that the angle of their axis can be varied. At the position where the roller axis is vertical to the drive shafts, the drive ratio is 1:1. Vary the axis and the ratios can be infinitely variable including

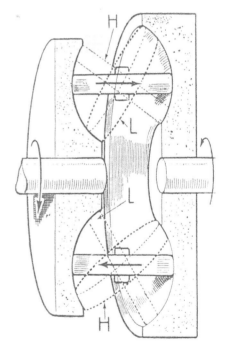

Diagram of the Hayes transmission variable gear for the 18hp Austin car, 1928-29

(Author)

overdrive. The whole unit is enclosed and filled with special lubricant. By means of a mechanism, which balances torque reaction against hydraulic pressure created by a pump, a roller will automatically adjust to the position to give the correct gear ratio. The ratio is constantly adjusted in accordance with the load imposed on the engine. There is also a manual override control which can be operated by the driver.

This was one of the non-aero-engine commissions received which helped to keep the office busy but, from now on, the two main streams of design activities the de Havilland Gipsy family and the Napier 'H' units, were to dominate the future years and the following chapter is devoted to the intense activities in the Halford design organisation up to the outbreak of the Second World War.

CHAPTER SEVEN

1929 – 1939 Developing the Gipsy series of engines

Standing in London's Piccadilly Circus and facing north, you could walk into Sherwood Street and, continuing for a few hundred yards, crossing Brewer Street enter Golden Square. In 1929, it was a quiet square of tall terraced buildings; the north side housing the Ear, Nose and Throat Hospital and many of the ground floor premises on the other sides occupied by the wholesale wool and tweed cloth trade. The centre of grass, flowers and trees enclosed by iron railings and accessible only to key-holders made a pleasant oasis of calm in central London.

The Halford consultancy moved into numbers 8 and 9 early in the year, occupying the fourth floor of No 8 and the fourth and fifth floors of No 9. As the fifth floor spanned both buildings, it housed the DH work along one side and the Napier work along the other at the front. The rear part provided offices for the checkers and the stress engineers. The fourth floor of No 8 contained the production drawing office and the print room, all under Basil Williams, to handle the modifications and, as was to follow with the use of the Tiger Moth as the standard RAF trainer, the issue of packages of approved changes in sufficient quantity for de Havilland to issue to all RAF units likely to be affected. The Golden Square offices proved to be very suitably sited and of sufficient size to meet future expansion for some years. The ground floor of No 8 was the showroom of Premier Drums, who supplied drum kits for the leading dance bands so popular in the twenties and thirties.

Foreign travel had not yet blossomed into the package holiday and business and commercial flying remained limited. What was then being designed in that London square was laying part of the foundations to bring air travel within the reach of many millions in the coming decades.

The atmosphere in the offices was a wonderful blend of enthusiasm, hard work, humour and an enormous dedication to the projects. It was not unusual for a designer to continue at his drawing board beyond normal working hours in order to get down on paper his ideas for the section of engine for which he was responsible while his mind was concentrated on the task and the design was coming along satisfactorily. Overtime pay was not expected or claimed, the additional hours being part of the enthusiasm for the work. Halford also handled a number of engineering projects not specifically related to aero-engines. Among these were the design of improved valve gears for at least two well-known makes of motor car.

It was a busy year and work developing the next Gipsy engine was well

Nos 8 and 9 Golden Square in 1994   (Author)

under way. This was the Gipsy II, an uprated version of the Gipsy I. The stroke was increased by half an inch, the valve gear enclosed in an oil bath and the power was increased to a maximum of 120 bhp at 2300 rpm. These changes meant an increase in piston speed and cylinders were re-designed as forgings in carbon steel, machined all over, and with closer-spaced cooling fins. The propeller thrust bearing on the front of the crankshaft was changed from a standard ball thrust race to a deep grooved journal type thrust race to prevent the balls moving radially and jamming when the propeller was windmilling when gliding. As airframes were developing, such as with the introduction of metal framework, engine design was modified; in this instance, by the use of mountings with rubber bushes to eliminate the transmission of vibration. The Gipsy II was the last upright engine.

1929 saw the Ghost engine off the drawing board. This was an eight-cylinder upright vee unit for use in the DH75 Hawk Moth, a four-seat high-wing cabin monoplane designed to meet an expected Commonwealth market. Alas, it was not a commercial success and only nine were built. America had various makes of similar types of machines and their then current economic depression enabled them to sell at prices with which de Havilland could not compete.

It was during this year that Halford suffered an unexpected tragic and great loss. His sister, Kathleen, of whom he was very fond, entered hospital for a routine operation from which she contracted blood poisoning due to the use of a contaminated needle. Halford rushed to her bedside and arranged for specialists from Harley Street to attend. Nothing could be done and she died at the age of thirty-two. The family were devastated – none more than her brother, Frank. The family commissioned the erection of a lych gate at the Church of the Holy Rood in their home village of Edwalton in Kathleen's memory.

Halford entered the 1930s with the introduction of an inverted engine (as he and Ricardo had done with the RHA engine in 1917) so improving the pilot's forward view and aiding the modern advance to streamlined aircraft. This emerged as the Gipsy III and set the future trend. Both the Gipsy II and III had cast-aluminium alloy crankcase and fitted with a Claudel-Hobson carburettor and twin BTH magnetos. With the inverted Gipsy III, the obvious problem was how to control the lubrication and avoid an accumulation of oil in the cylinders. This was satisfactorily achieved by extending the cylinder skirts into the crankcase, thereby preventing oil flowing into the cylinders. The use of an oil tank and pump feed in place of the wet sump, plus two large-bore oil return pipes – one at each end of the crankcase – and twin scavenging pumps to return the oil to the tank – was to prove very satisfactory under all flying conditions. With the success of the inverted engine, development in aircraft design imposed a need for further engine development. The bore was increased from 114mm to 118mm and this gave 130 bhp maximum output. In this period, the introduction of heavier metal propellers caused an increase of stress in the crankshaft and some redesign had to be undertaken.

1931 and 1932 saw the production of the Gipsy IV, a smaller engine of 3.9-litres capacity rated at 80 bhp, designed to power the DH81 Swallow Moth, but never went into production. Next came the Gipsy Major I, which was generated from the Gipsy III and became a reliable 130 bhp four-cylinder which could use the metal propeller. Cylinder heads were of aluminium bronze, the valves seating directly on the head, no valve seat inserts were fitted. Carburation was by a Claudel Hobson AI 48A down-draught carburretor. Over fourteen-thousand were produced and it was fitted to at least six types of de Havilland aircraft, in single and double units, the best known being the Tiger Moth, which became the most widely-used elementary trainer aircraft for the Services. By 1944, this engine could run for 1500 hours between overhauls.

The following years saw Halford even more absorbed in his work. Although he maintained regular contact with Monica and daughter Patricia, it was evident there was no chance of the marriage recovering and, in 1932, they divorced; Patricia living with her mother and often spending her school holidays with her grandmother at the White House.

To return to the progress of the Gipsy engine development, 1933 saw the emergence of the six-cylinder engines to provide units of 200 bhp. It was more practical to retain the bore and stroke of the four-cylinder engines (118 x 140mm) rather than try to get the greater power by increasing these sizes and this enabled many Major parts to be incorporated. Twin Claudel-Hobson carburretors were fitted – each supplying three cylinders. Lubrication was dry sump – the oil pumps and filters being part of a detachable unit bolted to the rear of the crankcase. The frontal area was to be kept as small as possible. One of the first problems to emerge was serious torsional vibration which caused a crankshaft failure between the two front cylinders. Torsiograph tests were taken and by using a revised firing order, the vibration stress was reduced very considerably and production engines were based on this revised firing order – 1.2.4.6.5.3 instead of 1.5.3.6.2.4. (The firing order of the BHP had been 1.5.3.6.2.4). This was the first series of the Gipsy Six.

In January 1934, Geoffrey de Havilland decided that Britain must be represented in the proposed England to Australia air race due to take place in October. The result was the beautiful DH88, a twin-engined low-wing monoplane, named the Comet. De Havilland required Halford to give him suitable engines for this venture. The Gipsy Six was selected and modifications put in hand to create the Gipsy Six 'R'. Because this was a long-distance speed event, it called for propellers with a pitch for fast

DH88 Comet Racer 1934   (Author)

cruising to get the best usage of fuel and a different pitch for take-off. A search for a two-pitch propeller which would be immediately available resulted in using the pneumatically-controlled French Ratier design. The standard engine was modified with high lift valve gear and high compression was achieved by machining some metal from the face of the cylinder heads, plus fitting pistons with higher crowns. Power was increased to 280 bhp at 2350 rpm. The use of the heavier variable-pitch propeller required changing from a tapered crankshaft extension to parallel splines. The whole effort, designing and building the team of Comet aircraft, modifying the Gipsy Six engines, obtaining and fitting the variable-pitch propellers and the numerous problems and teething troubles had to be completed in time for the scheduled start of the race on October 20.

Halford travelled to Mildenhall for the start of the race, scheduled for 5.00am. Among the well-wishers was Miss Florence Desmond, a famous actress and girlfriend of pilot, Tom Campbell-Black. At the start, she told him that if he won she would marry him. He did and she did!!! That the aircraft were successfully produced in ten months was an incredible achievement from all the de Havilland and Halford personnel. This was then emphatically confirmed by Charles Scott and Tom Campbell-Black arriving at Melbourne to win the speed race in their Comet *Grosvenor House* after a flight of 11,300 miles in a flying time of 60 hours, 50 mins, 18 secs.

The race itself threw up problems and, for the engine people, the story best remembered concerned Halford. He was on a bus in Regent Street on the morning Scott and Black were due in Darwin. The bus conductor pointed out the newspaper placard headlines that Scott and Black had retired from the race. Halford hurried back to Golden Square and was greeted by a Press Association journalist wanting an interview. By the greatest of good fortune, the Press Association had a telephone line open to Darwin and promptly gave it to Halford who was able to speak to Scott direct. The problem was that the oil gauge for one engine showed no pressure and they had crossed the Timor Sea with that engine shut down. Halford suspected piston trouble due to using cast pistons, because forged ones could not be obtained in time and suggested changing to standard pistons and keeping that engines throttled back. However, the DH mechanic from Sydney was available to deal with the trouble. He found that the cause of there being no oil pressure was due to a completely clogged Autoclean filter. This cleared the trouble, but the propeller had stuck in high pitch which caused a drop in engine revs of about 150 rpm. However, the flight was continued and, as history records, success was achieved.

At the time Halford raced back to the Golden Square office to talk on the telephone to Scott, his daughter was waiting to have lunch with him at the Cafe Royal. It was some little time before Halford remembered and managed to contact her for a somewhat later luncheon. But, as a result of the successful outcome of the race, Patricia's school gave a day's holiday to the pupils in celebration of this British victory. A fact for which she was very proud indeed. As a gesture of thanks to his staff and to celebrate the victorious finish to this epic aviation event, Halford closed the office and everyone had an extra day of holiday. In commemorating this event, the Royal Aeronautical Society presented him, in 1935, with its Silver Medal in recognition of his work on the Cirrus and Gipsy series of engines.

At the age of nine, Patricia was sent to boarding school and her mother taught dancing after her ballet career ended. Patricia was an accomplished tennis player having started from the age of eight. When she was ten, she entered junior tournaments and, five years later, she won the junior title at Eastbourne, the ladies' tournament held prior to Wimbledon. In 1936, she attended finishing school in Paris and continued tennis with a French coach. Her promising tennis career was cut short following an accident in which she suffered a broken pelvis.

The next two years, 1935 and 1936, were of significance in the development of the Gipsy series of engines. This particularly applied to the Gipsy Six series II which was fitted with a geared drive to the propeller to reduce its speed to three-quarters that of the crankshaft and obtain the best advantage from the use of the variable pitch. Compression had been increased to 6:1 and aluminium cylinder heads allowed leaded fuels to be used. In this series of six-cylinder engines, a variation of top crankcase covers were available to cater for the accessories related to specific aircraft. Although the general economic climate was dull and unemployment had risen as a result, there was a steady increase in overseas markets both for light aircraft and commercial airlines.

With the Gipsy engines now established and the refining of four- and six-cylinder units offering a range of powers from 120 to 300 bhp, certain factors were having a major impact on design. The obvious benefits derived from the use of variable-pitch metal propellers led de Havilland to enter the market in the UK and to create the de Havilland Propeller Company to build the American Hamilton Standard design under licence. This decision was taken in 1934 and the licence agreements were finalised in June of that year.

The impact of this on engine design emerged with the revised magnesium alloy cast crankcase Gipsy Major Series II and Six Series II. Development of the Major II ran parallel with the Six II and a number of design improvements were jointly adopted. It was the Gipsy Six which was first to be adapted for the variable-pitch propeller. A very extensive test programme was carried out before the unit entered into production. Torsional vibration

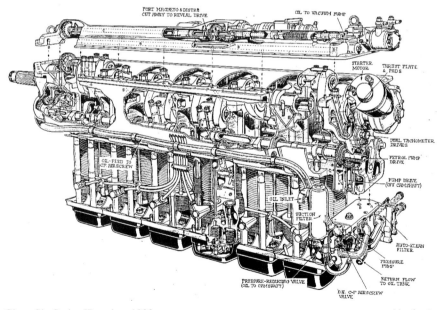

Gipsy Six Series II engine, 1933 (Author)

had reared its head with the six-cylinders as mentioned earlier and, at that time, a change in the firing order made a significant improvement, but now, with the advent of the new type of propeller, further investigation into torsional vibration was needed. Dr Kerr Wilson inaugurated an intensive study of engine dynamics. This led to the design of rotating pendulum vibration dampers fitted to the crankshaft balancing webs. The next area to be considered was the use of 77-octane fuel, using tetra-ethyl lead additive. This necessitated a change in crankshaft material from a 55 tons per sq inch alloy steel (S11) to 65 tons per sq inch (S81). Further changes were aluminium-alloy cylinder heads with high-expansion steel valve seat inserts, improved finning, repositioned exhaust ports, improved rocker gear, sparking plugs changed from 12mm to 14mm, with shrouded threads (to protect from the effects of the leaded fuel) and compression ratio raised to 6:1.

The pre-production test programme involved 1,000 hours of high-duty running on the test-bed. The first 400 hours were run on the dynamometer, the next 600 hours were run with the variable-pitch propeller fitted and the engine mounted in a special suspended cradle. Two tests of 100 hours each were then run at full throttle with the propeller pitched to absorb the power developed at 2400 rpm. Such tests far exceeded any possible stresses which would be encountered in flight. It was this approach to each stage of change which continued to provide the reliability for which Halford's designs were famous.

In 1935, the concept of a 500-horse power engine was initiated. This emerged as a twelve-cylinder inverted-vee air-cooled supercharged engine.

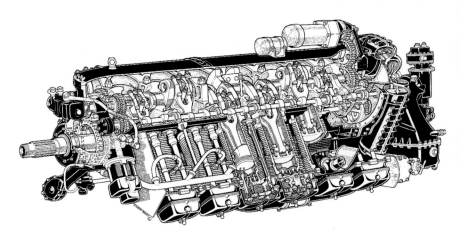

Gipsy Twelve 525bhp 1935 (Lyndon Jones)

DH91 Albatross airliner, 1935-36 – four Gipsy Twelve engines   (Peter Kirk)

This was based on two Six IIs. The crankcase was an Elektron casting. A reduction gear was incorporated into the main drive and a twin induction SU type AVT 25 carburettor which had automatic boost and mixture control. The Gipsy Twelve was the largest and most powerful of the Gipsy range. It produced its own problems, which were successfully dealt with, and four were fitted to power the de Havilland DH91 Albatross 20-23 seat airliner. One of the innovations introduced by Halford on the engine installation in the Albatross was reverse-flow air cooling which had the effect of reducing engine drag. This aircraft came into being in May 1937 and, at the end of 1938, were supplied to Imperial Airways for the London-Paris and London-Brussels routes. Later, the London-Alexandria route was added.

In 1936, the Silver Jubilee of the reign of King George V and Queen Mary was celebrated and great preparations were made. London's West End became filled with visitors from all the countries of the British Empire. To the members of Halford's staff, it was the opportunity of viewing the colourful and sometimes exotic uniforms of services from all the Empire countries. Another light-hearted benefit to being in Golden Square was that, at the fifth floor level, there was a good view, enhanced by binoculars, of the delightful young ladies of the Windmill Theatre chorus practising on the flat roof of the theatre in the summer months. Halford, at that time, would arrive in the office driving a straight-eight Packard drop-head coupe, a long maroon-coloured car, which he parked at the roadside each day at high speed, reversing into position with the unfailing accuracy of a racing driver, bounding into the building almost before the engine stopped.

There was one annual duty the staff always undertook and that was on the

89

eleventh of November when they would make their way to Piccadilly Circus and stand around the Eros statue. At the stroke of eleven, the maroons would be fired and the minute silence observed in remembrance of the dead of the First World War. Many of the staff had served in the Army and Air Force during that conflict and honoured their comrades before returning to their drawing boards and desks. It was always a very moving occasion.

De Havilland's were pressing Halford for a closer association, as their entire engine design was in his hands as an independent consultant. In 1937, de Havilland built a suite of offices as a separate single-storey building at their Stag Lane site. Halford moved from Golden Square, sending the staff who were involved on the Napier engines to the Napier Works at Acton, then transferred the remaining staff to the Stag Lane offices. He retained his independent status, paid rent to de Havilland for use of the offices and the existing system of remuneration for work was maintained. In addition to being alongside the engine works, he and his staff had access to the works and test-beds, for observation purposes only. Halford and Moult divided their time between Stag Lane and Acton while W S Arscott, as chief designer, spent his time on the Napier developments and was rarely seen at Stag Lane. The personnel who came to Stag Lane from Golden Square included Bill Cullen (installation engineer), Tom Winter (to become chief draughtsman), Johnny Johnston (in charge of the stress office) and Dr David Cockburn (compressor specialist). Another staff member, a drawings checker named Draper, was the son of the Napier tester who drove one of the three 60 hp Napier cars which took part in S F Edge's 24-hours Brooklands endurance run on 28/29 July 1907. After the event, Edge presented each driver with an inscribed gold watch and they kept the special leather flying suit-type coverall which were in the colour of their particular car. His son had inherited these mementoes and they were greatly treasured as part of motoring history. Basil Williams remained in charge of the production drawing office until 1938 when he took up a post with de Havilland in Australia, taking with him details of the DH constant-speed propeller and the drawings for the Gipsy Minor engine. He was charged with the task of getting these units into production.

In 1937, a new small engine had been produced, rated at 90 bhp. This was an inverted four-cylinder, the Gipsy Minor, designed to be one-third less weight than the existing four-cylinder units and specifically for installation in the DH94 Moth Minor. This was a two-seat, open-cockpit, low-wing monoplane to provide a basic, low-cost club machine for under £600. Production was terminated by the outbreak of the war and, in 1940, all drawings and parts were transferred to Australia where about 100 were built as training machines. With plans to increase the power to 100 bhp and incorporate an airscrew reduction gear, the Minor was set to become an economic and popular small engine. However, the war intervened.

During the 1920s and 1930s, there was a steady increase in the popularity of private flying generated by the numerous aero clubs which spanned the country. A number of types of light aircraft came onto the market, many powered by the Gipsy-series engines. The sport of competitive flying and record attempts by enthusiastic individuals became regular events and received wide publicity. One such event in September 1936 was the Schlesinger race from the UK to Johannesburg. Air Publicity Ltd entered a modified Percival Mew Gull G-AEKL, with a Gipsy Six series II engine and additional fuel tanks. The pilot selected was Tom Campbell-Black who, with Charles Scott, had crewed the de Havilland Comet to victory in the 1934 England-Australia MacRobertson race. On 19 September 1936, Campbell-Black flew the aircraft to Speke, the Liverpool Municipal Airport, in order to have the machine named *Miss Liverpool*. He flew several demonstration flights to thank those who backed his attempt, following which he prepared to fly back to London. Whilst taxiing out into position for take-off, he failed to see a Hawker Hart of No 611 Squadron RAF coming in to land. The pilot of the Hart could not see the Mew Gull due to the bulk of his Kestrel engine and the port wing of the Gull hit the port undercarriage of the Hart, which collapsed. The propeller of the Hart hit the port wing of the Gull and continued across the cockpit. Campbell-Black received fatal injuries and a great flying sportsman was lost.

The years 1927 through to 1938 were notable in the private aviation world for the attempts by courageous pilots in light aircraft to tackle long distance flights to be completed in the shortest time and set up a new record. Gipsy engines powered the 109 long distance flights (recorded in Appendix V) and, in addition, there was considerable success in the competitions held in between war years. Although the Gipsys had built up and maintained a reputation for reliability, an Air Ministry notice to aircraft owners and ground engineers dated August 1932 indicated the sort of unexpected snag likely to hit designer and manufacturer. This notice read:-

"Certain con-rods on early Gipsy I, II and III engines have embossed identification letters and numbers on the shank. A small number of failures has occurred due to fatigue cracks starting from the root of the letters and spreading laterally across the rod. Letters and numbers should be filed off and all traces of the embossing and file marks polished out."

Aircraft diesel engine projects

At the end of 1935 and continuing through to September 1940, the Halford team were active in considering the development of a diesel power unit for aircraft. Investigation into this area embraced a number of alternative schemes and, of necessity, required experimental test units to develop the all-important combustion efficiency and mechanical robustness that would be needed, coupled with that ever present headache of 'weight'. Poppet- and sleeve-valve units were considered. This field of development led Halford to contact his old friend, Sir Harry Ricardo, and considerable correspondence took place as ideas were translated into practical designs and test units prepared. With Ricardo's continuing development of diesel designs and his wealth of experience and recorded data, he responded to Halford's problems and provided expert analysis and guidance. Halford, Brodie and Moult were in regular contact with Sir Harry and his engineers. All this programme was done with the knowledge and agreement of the de Havilland Company Engine Division and Ricardo's were in receipt of fees for their involvement.

In November 1935, the initial layout drafted was of a 'Y' form three-cylinder, two-stroke, air-cooled, sleeve-valve radial engine of 100mm bore and 115mm stroke. This gave a total capacity of 2709cc and an estimated output of 70 bhp at 2000 rpm – compression ratio of 16:1. In parallel, a seven-cylinder radial side-valve was considered. Later in the month, there was a proposal to draft the design of a five-cylinder in-line and a ten-cylinder 45-degree-vee engine. However, development of the three-cylinder radial proceeded into 1936 and examination of the German Howald two-stroke schemes and patents were reviewed, but not taken further. In early April 1936, detail drawings were under way. In August, consideration of an adaptation of the Gipsy Six to a diesel configuration was seriously investigated. This coincided with de Havilland receiving very substantial orders from the Air Ministry for both Gipsy Sixes and Twelves, which had to be modified to conform to service requirements and then to pass service type-tests. This left no possibility for pursuing diesel development and Halford's desire to co-operate with Ricardo on a civil diesel aircraft had to be shelved as service needs absorbed de Havilland experimental and production capacity. Before this happened, it was evident that de Havilland were very interested and supportive of the diesel idea.

It was not until early 1937 that time became available to take up the matter again. The re-emergence of a Gipsy Six diesel came into prominence with investigation into using the Ricardo patented Comet Mark III cylinder head. This design provided a swish chamber above the crown of the head into which inlet air was forced via a narrow entry throat, with the fuel injector being fitted into the swish chamber. The resultant swirl of the air and fuel provided an efficient combustion mixture. This type of head has been in continuous use and improved over the years by the Ricardo organisation and is currently, as Marks VII and VIII, still incorporated in engines today.

Applying this principal to the Gipsy Six meant that compression ratios of 16.5:1 had to be considered. It must be remembered that during these years the development of the Napier Dagger and sleeve-valve Sabre was vigorously underway and the application of sleeve-valves to the aircraft diesel was part of the embryo design programme.

By October 1938, a single-cylinder two-stroke experimental unit was being prepared after agreement between Halford and Geoffrey de Havilland that pursuance of diesel development would be of marketable benefit to the de Havilland Company. Before the end of the year, the Halford team had made preliminary investigations into a number of various diesel configurations for high-power units, including a four-cylinder, two-stroke, sleeve-valve of 102mm bore and 115mm stroke, a ten-cylinder, two-stroke, inverted-vee engine of the same bore and stroke, to give an output of 365 bhp at 2400 rpm, and a twelve-cylinder, two-stroke, inverted vee engine to provide a take-off power of 467 bhp at 2500 rpm and a cruising power of 312 bhp at 1800 rpm.

In 1939, the diesel-based programme continued and, in March, the five-cylinder inverted in-line poppet-valve diesel to give 150 bhp at 2300 rpm was brought to the fore, based on the idea of replacing the Gipsy Major engine in the Tiger Moth trainer.

At the end of September, the Air Ministry gave de Havilland instructions that progress in the development of the two-stroke diesel was of great importance and should be given high priority, but this directive was shortly set aside as the more immediate war needs took priority. With the coming of the gas turbine engines and the rapid development of this high-powered unit for commercial aircraft, plus the fact that post-war light aircraft were well catered for by the small petrol-fuelled conventional piston engine, the diesel plans were not revived.

Continuing the development programme in 1938, an experimental six-cylinder – the Gipsy Six 3 Ex – was on the drawing board based on the Six I. This was to be the basis for future Sixes. Bore and stroke increased from 118mm x 140mm to 120mm x 150mm, compression ratio of 6.5:1 and maximum speed was 2500 rpm. In line with the Six 3 Ex development, the Gipsy Major 2A followed similar lines. Parallel to the Six 3 Ex, a high-speed six design was drafted as a 'square' engine of 110mm bore and stroke, supercharged and fuel-injected. Incorporated in this engine for the first time was Halford's patented hydraulic tappets developed by de Havilland. The patent was licensed to the Eaton Manufacturing Co, USA, who made the 'Zerolash' hydraulic tappets. Halford's patent design became the basis for many future aero and car engines hydraulic tappets.

By 1938, the family of Gipsy engines had reached a total of fifteen in eleven years and their history of reliability is a major tribute to Halford's skills. These designs all had to fill a particular niche in the market and were designed to be produced at a competitive price in the growing aviation business. Cost efficiency was achieved, not only by detail design to simplify the manufacture of parts, but by the interchangeability of parts throughout the range of engines. This also simplified maintenance. Geoffrey de Havilland had made a shrewd decision when he put his Company's engine design in the sole and independent hands of Frank Halford.

The Halford organisation came into 1939 with a busy programme of development. Early in 1939, design work on an uprated Gipsy Twelve started aimed at a power output of 800 bhp. Continuing development of the Major and Six series was maintained in the form of the first supercharged Six (Gipsy Six 3S). This led to it becoming the Gipsy Queen 4 following flight-testing in an Airspeed Oxford in March 1941. Engines modified to conform to Ministry requirements were identified as the Queen series.

The little Minor engine was a very successful venture and held great promise for the future. A diesel single-cylinder test unit was on the test-bed and torsional vibration control had advanced with Dr Kerr Wilson as the acknowledged expert. At this time, he was completing his definitive book which, even today, remains the basic guide on this subject.

In June 1939, Halford and Ricardo reported to the Engine Sub-Committee of the Aeronautical Research Committee of their findings relating to proposals for work on a two-stroke petrol-injection engine. They were of the opinion that results obtained so far were not sufficiently far in advance of those now obtained from the Sabre engine. This was one of Halford's

"Monkbarns", Northwood, Middlesex Home of FBH family from 1939   (Patricia Draper)

numerous involvements in various investigations on behalf of the Air Ministry. The RAF expansion programme had at last got underway and, following the crisis with Hitler's Germany in 1938, the risk of war loomed nearer.

During 1939, Halford's personal life entered a new phase. In August, he remarried. Majorie Moore had been a friend for some years. Following their marriage, Halford bought a house at Sandy Lane, Northwood, in Middlesex. They moved into *Monkbarns* in early September and were to remain there during Halford's lifetime. The property was conveniently situated within easy reach of both the Stag Lane offices at Edgware and the de Havilland headquarters at Hatfield.

In September, Patricia returned from France and spent some time with her grandmother at the White House. It was on Sunday 3 September she attended service with her grandmother at the Church of the Holy Rood when the vicar suddenly interrupted the service to announce that war had been declared.

When the design staff returned to Stag Lane after the weekend, it was to find that all current work was suspended pending further instructions from the Air Ministry. The office remained in a vacuum for the next five weeks; made more frustrating by the requirement to attend seven days a week until further orders. The time was spent in 'tidying up' the current projects.

Halford's design commitments increased to the extent that his responsibilities severely curtailed his time for social activities. Up to 1934, he had been regularly involved in his passion for motor racing, mainly at the Brooklands track, and had enjoyed a successful career behind the wheel. He was, like his daughter, a good tennis player and enjoyed squash. He was never a very keen team sportsman, unlike his father, and did not take part in team games. However, as his father and grandfather had done, he actively supported Notts County Football Club and was a director from June 1939, resigning in February 1945 due to his post-war involvement as a Director of the de Havilland Engine Company. Whenever possible, he enjoyed watching the County team with friends, waxing enthusiastic during play. He was an accomplished ballroom dancer on social occasions; the fact that he became portly in middle age did not detract from his nimble efforts on the dance floor.

CHAPTER EIGHT

1928 – 1943 Designing for D Napier & Son

The long and varied history of D Napier & Son Ltd, founded in 1808, had by 1928 reached a crossroads and the directors had to decide on which market the future of the Company should be based. The choice before them was either to return to car manufacture, continue with aero-engines or enter an entirely new field. The idea of returning to motor cars was ruled out as the motor industry had, by this time, expanded into providing a wide range of models covering luxury to smaller 'popular' cars. Napiers felt the luxury market was already well provided for and they were not in a position to mass-produce less expensive models. In any case, they had never been a company based on that type of engineering.

The Napier Lion aero-engine, designed by M S Napier and A J Rowledge in 1917 and steadily developed and improved, had enjoyed very successful sales through the first ten years but it was obvious that it would be in diminishing demand as new types of aircraft were on the drawing board, which would require different power units. An exception to this was the marine version, the Sealion, for which the demand remained buoyant and indeed continued to be produced as the power unit for RAF air-sea rescue launches used during World War II. The production of the aero Lion was continued in small numbers until 1932 as the Series XV, rated at 555 bhp at 2350 rpm.

The Board decided to continue with aero-engine design and manufacture. The major concern was who should undertake the design of a new line of engines. They believed they could no longer expect Montague Napier, who was in poor health and for that reason lived in the South of France, to be able to shoulder such a burden and A J Rowledge had left the company in 1921. It would be necessary to look outside the company for design and this resulted in an approach to Frank Halford. He was well known to A J Rowledge, who had been replaced by Capt George S Wilkinson as chief designer. Wilkinson was aware of Halford's designs in the aero-engine field and his successful record. This line of enquiry received the support of Montague Napier and discussions were instigated to map out the types of engine likely to fulfil the needs of the industry and essentially the military requirements in the future. As an independent consultant, Halford was interested in involvement in Napier's plans but only on condition he kept his independence and stipulated Napier's right to manufacture air-cooled engines of his design provided their cylinder capacity was between 404.09 cubic inches and 718.37 cubic inches; this ensuring these designs did not conflict with any other commitments he had, with de Havilland for instance. He commenced as a design consultant for Napiers in 1928 and initiated the creation of a series of engines of greater power and complexity, developing along very different lines to his previous undertakings.

At the time Napiers were drawing up the agreement with Halford, they became keen on the possibilities suggested by the compression-ignition engine for aviation. Should they choose to pursue this area they knew they would have to pay for outside experience and eventually, in 1930, they negotiated with Junkers and Treiber of Germany. A licence from Junkers enabled the manufacture and marketing by 1934 of two opposed-piston diesels, the Cutlass and the Culverin, but they generated little interest and few sales and were eventually discontinued.

In the meantime, Halford was progressing with the designs of engines which became known as 'H' engines due to their configuration of two parallel banks of opposed cylinders. In August 1930, reviewing the power needs of light aircraft, Napiers induced Halford to design a six-cylinder in-line engine and set aside a sum of £50,000 for this purpose. An early return on the investment was expected to bring in much-needed profits. Montague Napier died in January 1931 and his agreement in 1928 to obtain the services of Halford was proving to be of essential value for the continuance and profitability of the Company.

The aero-engine industry was gathering pace from 1929 onwards and

Napier Javelin 6-cylinder 135bhp 1932 (Author)

large radials were competing with the Lion. Rolls-Royce was continuing to produce in-line-vee engines which gave aircraft designers the smaller frontal areas modern streamlining required. This meant an increasing dependence on Napier's agreement with Halford for the six-cylinder engine of 135 bhp at 2100 rpm. It came onto the market in 1932 as the E97 and, after some modifications in 1933, was called the Javelin. It was never made in great numbers, but was used experimentally in several types of aircraft including the British Klemm Eagle, Percival Gull Four II and the Mew Gull I. Production ceased in 1935.

Halford had been working steadily since 1928 on the 16-cylinder 'H' layout and, at about the time of Montague Napier's death, the 300 bhp Rapier engine was well advanced. He had consulted with the Air Ministry as to their future service requirements of a high-powered unit for installation in an interceptor fighter, possibly a de Havilland aircraft, which led him to the concept of the multi-cylinder, twin-crankshaft, 'square' engine (bore and stroke equal). Halford's design was in millimetres, but Napier's converted to

Napier Rapier 16-cylinder H engine 390bhp　　　　　　(Napier Power Heritage Trust)

inches, possibly because they were tooled up in inches and their machinists and fitters were more conversant with tolerances in 'thous' of an inch.

Development of an engine so advanced as the Rapier produced problems in design, calling for rethinking and research. As this was a two-crankshaft engine, bearing loadings, balance of reciprocating and rotating parts, torsional vibration, the choice of crank assemblies and firing order all required investigation before a final combination could be selected as the most effective and reliable design.

One of the major areas of concern was to find a satisfactory bearing material. At that time, a white-metal lining in a steel half-shell was the norm. Many other combinations were tried. Halford was on a visit to America and spoke with friends from General Motors who suggested the use of 'Allison Bronze' as developed by their Allison Division. As a result, Napiers manufactured lead-bronze bearings which proved to be satisfactory providing the filter system in the oil supply eliminated all solid matter. This led to coating the soft lead surface with indium. Following this, a combination of copper-lead-indium surface on a continuous strip was developed and produced by G A Vandervell. These were the famous 'thin wall bearings'.

In 1929, the Rapier was uprated to 400 bhp and installed in the DH77 fighter. However, although it had a high performance, the aircraft did not go into production. Subsequently, the Rapier powered the Fairey Sea Fox, which saw service in the Second World War. The unusual Mayo composite aircraft, with a small aircraft mounted on top of a flying boat, used four Rapiers in the upper component. Major Mayo's idea of getting a high performance aircraft with a commercial payload into the air by launching it from a larger machine after the composite unit had taken off was a brilliant scheme at that time of limited power availability and lack of long runways. This aircraft, the Short Mercury, successfully flew the Atlantic with a payload in 1938 from Foynes via Montreal to New York in 22½ hours and later broke the long distance record by flying 6000 miles non-stop to South Africa.

Hot on the heels of the Rapier, Halford started work on the next generation of large-power engines for Napier, expanding on his ideas of H-type layouts into the 24-cylinder Dagger. This design included hydraulic self-adjusting tappets in the valve-operating gear and so reduced the time taken for servicing. The air-cooled Dagger was supercharged and timed as a 24-cylinder engine whereas the later Sabre was timed as two 12-cylinder units. Developed versions of the Dagger followed with the Dagger II fully supercharged at 670-695 bhp at 3500 rpm at 10,000 ft and experimentally installed in the Hawker Hart and the Dagger III, a medium supercharged engine giving 700-725 bhp at 3500 rpm at 3500 ft. Development continued

Short Mayo composite – the upper component Mercury fitted with four Rapier engines
(Rolls-Royce Heritage Trust)

Napier Dagger 24-cylinder 800bhp, 1934   (Napier Power Heritage Trust)

to the Dagger VIII, fitted with a double-entry supercharger and rated at 890-925 bhp at 4000 rpm at 9000 ft. Various versions of the Dagger were installed in the Fairey Battle, Handley Page Hereford, Hawker Hart, Hawker Hector and Martin Baker MB2.

Designing a 1000 hp engine with capability for development of considerable greater power output based on multiple small bore and short-stroke cylinders enabled higher engine speeds to be attained at the crankshaft, but this was of no use if coupled direct to the propeller and so a reduction gear had to be used. This brought the problem of designing a gearing system which could cope with the transmission of the power and not impose too high gear tooth stresses. Size and weight also required careful consideration. The solution was found by taking the power from each crankshaft into layshafts, the front ends of which geared to a sun gear driving the propeller. To control gear tooth loading, it was necessary to use a combination of spur gears and helical gears. This is an example of the problems facing designers when reaching into unexplored areas and the degree of anticipatory thought which must be imposed at the drawing board and the stress office.

After seven years, Halford's efforts were showing a strong return to the aero-engine industry for the Napier Company and, furthermore, a return to healthy profits. In 1935, the Directors made a powerful approach to Halford to join the Board as Technical Director. He eventually agreed to do so, but was not that comfortable in accepting an appointment which reduced his independence. By 1935, the expansion of the RAF was taking its initial steps and the Air Ministry ordered ninety Daggers at £2800 each. During 1936, the aircraft industry indicated there would be a need for engines of 2000 bhp.

In September 1937, the Air Ministry – through Major Bulman – agreed to Halford's request and allowed data on the Dagger to be sent to Ricardo to draw on his expertise. Ricardo had been engaged over a number of years during the 1920s into the 1930s, at his Shoreham works, on Air Ministry-sponsored projects related to the possible advantages of the sleeve-valve engine both in petrol and diesel form. The Ministry were particularly interested in high-power aero-engine application and, as the results of the project emerged, their interest veered in favour of the petrol version. This had now reached a stage where the Ministry were satisfied that the advantages of the sleeve-valve should be applied to development of large aero-engines and they made Ricardo's twelve years' work available to engine manufacturers, together with his willing continuing co-operation. Halford continued to consult Ricardo, particularly in regard to his design of the engine which was to follow the Dagger, and considerable correspondence and meetings were in evidence from October 1936 resulting in a twin-opposed cylinder-sleeve valve unit being built and tested at Acton, together with a single-cylinder unit, tests showing encouraging results. At the same time, the use of glycol for cooling was under investigation.

In considering how to get a power unit of 2000 bhp and over, many options were explored. Finally, the 24-cylinder H-type was retained but turned through ninety degrees, cylinders being horizontal and crankshafts one above the other. With the increase in engine speeds, the use of valves posed difficulties and the decision to use single sleeve valves was taken based on the test unit results. The Javelin, Rapier and Dagger were air-cooled units but in this engine air-cooling would be inadequate, so water-cooling was introduced with the water pump underneath the engine and the headers on top. The Sabre had begun its difficult progress to becoming the world's most powerful piston aero-engine of the day. This was a 36.7 litre engine which, with a single-stage, double-sided impeller, centrifugal supercharger, gave 2200 bhp at 3700 rpm and weighing 2360 lb. January 1938 saw the Sabre pass its two-hour test and the Air Ministry took control of the development programme.

During 1938, Napiers started an unusual development when they undertook their first design concept by A E Hagg, who had come from de Havilland Aircraft Co, to produce an aircraft to challenge the world landplane speed record. Hagg's idea was based on a low-wing monoplane of advanced conception. As Napier did not have staff able to produce the necessary aircraft design, they approached the Heston Aircraft Company whose chief designer, George Cornwall, undertook the work, the intention being to use this initial Sabre engine as the power source. Financial support was forthcoming from a generous Lord Nuffield. The machine became known as the Napier-Heston Racer. This was a beautiful machine of wooden construction. A trial flight by Squadron Leader G L G Richmond, Heston's chief test pilot, ran into trouble after a few minutes when the engine overheated due to defective airflow through the cooling system. He made an approach to land but stalled and the machine was irretrievably damaged.

By July 1940, the Sabre achieved an excellent type-test and the, by then, Ministry of Aircraft Production raised its production priority and large orders followed. To reach this stage had taken four-and-a-half years from the initial lines being made on the drawing board. As Napier entered the production phase, problems with sleeve manufacture came to the fore. The Burt and McCollum sleeve design owed its success to manufacturing accuracy and suitable material. Halford had specified chrome-molybdenum steel with a hardened belt on the inside diameter at the top of the stroke, but distortion and ovalising up to 0.008/0.010 inch was occurring. Silver plating was tried with no improvement. Production was delayed and engines were failing the two-hour testing. Air Commodore Banks at the Ministry suggested Halford consult with Bristols who had many year's experience of sleeve manufacture. Banks arranged with Rowbotham of Bristol to make two sleeves for the Sabre from Taurus forgings. Sabre sleeves were lasting 20-30 hours before unacceptable wear. Bristol sleeves of nitrided austenitic steel lasted 60 hours.

The Ministry, on the advice of Bristol, acquired the Sundstrand machine tool from the USA for machining the sleeves and these were installed at Napier's Liverpool factory. The Sabre had emerged as a difficult and multi-problem design which absorbed time and effort in the extreme before it was ready to go into manufacture and provide a reliable power unit in service. It was but one of the current high-powered engines with development problems. Other engines, including the Rolls-Royce Vulture and the Bristol Centaurus, were having initial problems.

During 1939, investigating work had been undertaken by Halford in conjunction with Ricardo on a two-stroke petrol-injection design of high power. This became of interest to the Aeronautical Research Committee who commissioned a report by the Engine Sub-Committee which was submitted to the Research Committee on 13 June 1939. The report indicated that results obtained by Ricardo on the test-bed units did not show improvement over that now available from the Sabre. In view of the report and the amount of development that would be required to produce a viable design, the Committee recommended cancelling the project.

Development work on the Sabre was ongoing and a steady series of variants were designed resulting in the following series:-

Sabre Variants
Series I   Development engine. Installed in three Folland 43/37, Napier-Heston Racer and Typhoon prototype
Series II   Production version for Hawker Typhoon, with SU carburettor

Series IIA	Position of sparking plugs changed. Extensive production. Installed in Typhoon 1B rated at 2180 bhp at 3700 rpm.
Series IIB	Uprated to 2220 bhp for Typhoon 1B and Tempest V
Series IIC	Installed in Tempest TT.V
Series III	Variant for installation in Blackburn Firebrand – 2300 bhp at 4000 rpm.
Series IV	Variant for Blackburn N2/42 flying boat, Tempest P
Series V	With Hobson-RAE injection carburettor – 2420 bhp at 3750 rpm

The following series were post Halford period.

Series VA	Two-speed supercharger rated at 2600 bhp at 3650 rpm at 6500 ft
Series VI	Modified VA with annular nose radiator and engine-driven cooling fan
Series VII	Further development of the VA with water/methanol injection and local strengthening. Rated at 2760 hp at 12500 ft (3055 bhp take-off) for installation in Hawker Fury.

Sabres were installed for development purposes in the Blackburn Firebrand, Fairey Battle, Folland 43/37 and Fury, Martin Baker MB3,

Napier Sabre Series V 24-cylinder H engine 2420bhp, 1937   (Napier Power Heritage Trust)

Vickers Warwick and in Typhoon and Tempest production aircraft.

When Halford relinquished his directorship with the Napier Company (see below), Napier's design engineers continued to develop his Sabre project and were successful in achieving considerable improvements in power output. It is interesting to compare the production costs of the three major engines of the period:

Rolls-Royce-built Merlins	£1 per bhp
Bristol Hercules	£2 per bhp
Napier Sabre	£4-5 per bhp

With the continuing development of the Gipsy series engines for de Havilland and the advent of jet propulsion work from 1941, Halford resigned from the Napier Board but kept his commitment to continue development work for Napier until 1943, when he and his organisation became part of the de Havilland Aircraft Company. When Halford took up his design appointment with Napier, their very existence had depended on his ability to produce the designs for a series of engines in tune with the needs of the market and the Ministry. He completely fulfilled those requirements.

A review of his professional life to date shows an amazing intensity of involvement. He was thirty-four years of age when, in 1928, he first undertook design work for Napier and, at the same time, was increasingly designing for de Havilland. This meant creating an organisation of his own, the selection of suitably experienced staff and, being the character he was, keeping personally involved and directing each and every one of them. He never eased his workload and was always in a position of knowing the detailed situation of all the work in hand and always gave a lead to finding practical solutions to any problems encountered.

CHAPTER NINE

1939 – 1945 The war and the de Havilland Engine Company

At the outbreak of the war, all work of a civil nature at the Stag Lane design office stopped on the orders of the Air Ministry and staff put on a seven-day week standby. For the next five weeks, there was nothing for people to do but wait for instructions. With the tense atmosphere created by declaration of war, it was a most frustrating time as everyone was champing at the bit to do something. A number of staff who were in the reserve forces were called up, only to return after a few weeks, reclassified as being in a reserved occupation; the Air Ministry deeming that their experience would serve the country better by continuing aero-engine development.

At last a project arrived. This first and most urgent requirement was the Auxiliary Generating Unit. It was necessary to provide as quickly as possible a means of dealing with the magnetic mines, sown in some numbers by the Germans in the shipping lanes around our coast. These mines remained on the sea bed until a metal-hulled ship passed over, which then caused the mine to explode by the use of magnetic fusing device. Actual contact between the mine and ship was not needed to set it off. The means to combat this menace was to equip a Wellington bomber with a 48 ft diameter magnetic 'degaussing' coil fitted below the wings of the aircraft, the coil being charged with electrical current produced by a generator housed in the aircraft's fuselage. This was a hair-raising process for the pilot and crew as both airspeed and altitude had to be such that by flying just about wave height the mine would be attracted and explode and the aircraft achieve sufficient distance beyond the blast area to remain unaffected.

The need for urgent results meant that this generator set had to be built with existing components. Halford selected the Gipsy Six engine, fitted with a speed governor and coupled to a London trolleybus motor converted into a generator, mounted on a simple steel channel section base frame. The first unit was ready for installation within six weeks. It proved to be a very successful operation and some seventeen aircraft were so fitted – some of which were later transferred to the Middle East to perform the same sweeping operation over the Suez Canal.

With the build up of the air war and following Dunkirk, de Havilland became involved in the repair of the Rolls-Royce Merlin engines. A number of satellite factories were set up within a close radius of the Stag Lane works and a few of Halford's people were temporarily seconded to assist the de Havilland engineers to set up these repair shops. This vital repair work continued unabated until 1944 and over 9000 Merlins were put through the shops.

Shot-down enemy aircraft were, of course, subject to intense scrutiny. Engines were removed and sent to various aero-engine companies to be dismantled and examined in the greatest detail. Reports were then prepared on the findings and forwarded to the Ministry of Aircraft Production and the Royal Air Force. De Havilland were involved in this activity and a number of German engines, including Mercedes Benz, BMW, Junkers and other types, arrived at Stag Lane hidden under covers in RAF trucks. Housed alongside the test-beds, engines were stripped down completely in the presence of DO and stress office representatives from Halford's office, who were responsible for carrying out the technical appraisal. There was particular interest in the use of serrated nuts which, being circular, were of smaller external dimension than the usual hexagonal type and, in addition to being lighter, did not require the clearance needed by conventional nuts for access. In a captured set of pilots' documents, it was found that, in common with allied practice, cold starting was assisted by the introduction of fuel into the oil supply to reduce viscosity and achieve quicker take-off in cold conditions, the fuel evaporating once the engine reached running temperature.

One particular fitting found on some captured aircraft provided the opportunity for our pilots to deal with the enemy by using knowledge of this to their advantage. This was a clockwork mechanism attached to the throttle control in the cockpit, its purpose being to limit the pilot's use of full boost on supercharged engines. Its operation allowed a three or four minute period on full boost, then cutting out and preventing re-engagement until a further two to three minutes had elapsed. This may have saved overstressing the engine but left the pilot vulnerable to our fighters where access to full boost was left to the discretion of the pilot. Once this information was distributed to our fighter squadrons, they could seek opportunities of forcing the enemy to use his full power, then waiting for the cut-out period, leaving him without the means of escape from a faster aircraft using full boost. However, monitoring enemy engine design in the early years of the war rarely produced surprises. It must be remembered that up to the commencement of hostilities, the free availability of technical data on a world-wide basis meant a detailed awareness of the direction in which aviation development in other countries was going.

To Halford, the major design effort at this period was centred on the Dagger and Sabre at Napiers. The complexity of these four-bank, twin-crankshaft, high-power units, particularly the sleeve-valve designs were providing problems to be solved. His successful Gipsy Series of both four-, six- and twelve-cylinder engine types were now engaging de Havilland production capacity to its maximum to fulfil orders for training and transport aircraft.

The Blitz was at its height during 1940 and some members of the design staff had volunteered for the de Havilland section of the LDV (Local Defence Volunteers – later to be renamed the Home Guard). They were issued with a 'uniform' consisting of a brown boilersuit, an arm band with the letters LDV and a tin hat. Those with First World War service or who had enlisted in the Territorial Army were the ones issued with a 1914-18 Lee-Enfield rifle. As two senior designers had been machine-gunners in the First World War, they were appointed to man the Vickers machine-gun, the tripod of which became a permanent addition on the flat roof of the single-storey office building. When the air-raid warning sounded, all LDVs gathered their kit and rifle, kept under their drawing boards, and ran to the rear window of the main DO, outside which was a catladder giving access to the roof and took up defensive positions on the roof. The machine-gun did get one opportunity to fire, at a low flying German bomber and they swore they scored a hit. The plane crashed some miles away, but the credit for the kill went to an anti-aircraft battery.

One excitement occurred when, after the all-clear sounded, a shot was heard in the building. It turned out to be the doorkeeper, a time-expired soldier who, when loading his gun, forgot he had 'one up the spout' and pulled the trigger. Fortunately, the rifle was pointing towards the open front doors. The bullet missed the houses opposite and winged its way to the north. The poor chap suffered having his leg pulled unmercifully and had to account for being one bullet short of quota. Later in the year, it was deemed prudent to disperse some units of the engine design organisation and the Stress Office staff were moved to a large detached house in a pleasant area of Mill Hill.

It was in 1940 at the height of the German bombing of London, when Halford contacted his ex-wife and his daughter who were living in a fifth floor flat in Kensington; Patricia working for the Red Cross nearby. He

Patricia with father at Monkbarns, 1939
(Patricia Draper)

insisted they leave London that night and not sleep in the basement of their flats as they usually did during air-raids. He was so persistent they stayed with friends at Harrow. On returning the next morning, they found their block of flats had received a direct hit and the bomb had penetrated the basement. Halford afterwards claimed he had a premonition of impending disaster. It undoubtedly saved their lives.

Halford was beginning to suffer from thrombosis in his legs, necessitating weeks of bed-rest at *Monkbarns*. He was not a good patient! He never stopped working and a sliderule was a permanent item on the bedside table. This condition was a recurring problem which he considered "just a damnable nuisance".

The Jet Engine

> *"Scientific investigation into the possibilities of jet propulsion has given no indication that this method can be a serious competitor to the airscrew engine combination ..."*
>
> The British Under-Secretary of State for Air (1934)

This unfortunate statement was made four years after Frank Whittle filed his first patent for a 'gas turbine in combination with jet reaction propulsion' and could have been responsible for the attitude towards the degree of official support he received in later years.

Aero-engine design had progressed with the internal combustion engine in a manner which, to an expert observer, indicated that future development would depart from the piston engine, which had to transfer reciprocating motion into rotary motion, to something of greater efficiency and capable of greater power. It was already known that the emission of hot exhaust gases from backward-facing exhausts could provide a propulsive effect if suitable exhaust emission nozzles were provided. If, therefore, air was compressed, fuel injected into the compressed air ignited and emitted as a high velocity jet, forward thrust or reaction force, would occur. So that, with a turbine and compressor of sufficient size, the resultant thrust of the continuous expelled gases would be able to provide the power required for the propulsion of aircraft.

The first practical proposal, in this country, to use a gas turbine as a power unit for aircraft came from the Royal Aeronautical Establishment in 1926 with the issue of a report by Dr A A Griffith entitled, 'An Aerodynamic Theory of Turbine Design'. Examination by the Establishment's selection committee resulted in approval to commence preliminary experiments, and a single-stage turbine, driving a single-stage compressor, both of axial-flow design, had been built during 1929. This had been supported by wind tunnel tests on cascades of compressors and tests of turbine blades during 1926 and 1927. Results were successful but approval to carry out further construction was not given and no work on gas turbines was done at RAE from 1930 to 1937. In March of 1937, the subject of gas turbines was resurrected and instructions issued to proceed with the development of a gas turbine driving a propeller and using axial-flow compressors and turbines in preference to the centrifugal type.

The gas turbine became a practical reality thanks to the perseverance of Frank Whittle. The story of his struggle to develop his ideas and produce a prototype engine on the test-bed are told in his own book, 'Jet.' It was not until 1935/6 that he was able to make further progress. The opportunity to raise finance enabled the company Power Jets Limited to be formed. Power Jets contracted the manufacture of a prototype engine to British Thompson Houston (BTH). By 1937, test-bed running of this first engine commenced and became a prolonged programme of experiment and modification which brought improvements as this new field of power production emerged as a practical engine for aircraft propulsion.

The story of Halford's introduction and involvement into gas turbine jets has been recorded by Dr Eric Moult who wrote of the following episode:

In 1938, John Brodie and Eric Moult were visiting Vauxhall Motors at Luton to meet with a long-term friend, Maurice Platt, who had been technical editor of The Motor and was now the Power Plant Engineer at Luton. Their purpose was to study General Motors' practice of shot-peening valve springs which was said to reduce the risk of fatigue failures. Also on the agenda was Maurice Platt's interest in the use of high-octane fuel and combating the problems arising from the inclusion of tetra-ethyl lead (TEL). The inclusion of a very small amount of TEL, about one half of one percent, to the fuel enabled compression ratios to be raised by a significant percentage, and a valuable increase of power resulted. However, as with many such benefits, there were corresponding disadvantages, such as burning and pitting of valve seats, so a balance had to be struck in order that additional power was not obtained at the expense of reliability. As this ground had been well explored by Halford's team and the assurance with which he could meet design power output and retain the now legendary reliability were sound reasons for Maurice Platt to seek their advice. To conclude their informal meeting, Platt took them on a tour of the experimental shops. Moult noticed a machine on which was mounted an unmistakable impeller for a centrifugal compressor of unusual large size. He mentioned this to Platt and the fact that it was something very unusual for Vauxhall. Platt, embarrassed, took them back to his office and begged them to say nothing as it was very secret.

Frank B Halford

John L Brodie

Eric Moult

The Team, 1930s-1950s

(Author)

A few days later, Platt phoned Moult and said he had permission to speak about this impeller work and would like advice on certain aero-engine accessories and the design of large castings in magnesium alloy, as Halford's team had had some experience in this field with the large Gipsy Twelve crankcase. Maurice Platt was invited to visit Stag Lane and given such help as was possible.

It transpired that the Ministry had asked Vauxhall to help in the production of the Whittle W2 engine. This was in the early days before Rover were involved. At this stage, Sir Henry Tizard contacted Halford requesting that he look into jet propulsion generally and the Whittle design in particular and report his views as to its application as an aircraft powerplant. Halford and his team went to meet Frank Whittle at Power Jets and also to see what BTH were doing at Rugby. They received every consideration and assistance from the pioneering team and were privy to the data accumulated from the Power Jets experiments and tests. Halford's report to Tizard stated that he had been very encouraged by what he had seen, but a much increased effort would be needed if such an engine were to be any use in the war. Tizard's response was to ask Halford to discuss possibilities with de Havilland.

Whittle's progress at Power Jets led, in 1939, to the Air Ministry giving approval for the RAE to start investigating the possibilities of both the Whittle 'counter-flow' centrifugal compressor engine and the RAE axial compressor design. In November 1940, Lord Beaverbrook, Minister of Aircraft Production, requested Ricardo to visit Power Jets and see if he could assist in speeding up the work. Ricardo gave unsparingly of his time and effort, supported by his company, in any areas of the development programme in which he could usefully contribute. In 1940, the Air Ministry sent a full set of drawings of the Whittle engine to Halford at Stag Lane. These drawings had been provided by the Rover Motor Company, who had earlier in the year, together with BTH, been given a production contract.

The involvement in gas turbine design for aircraft was also taking place in Germany when, in August 1939, the Heinkel He178 first flew for ten minutes. Obviously, much improvement would be necessary to obtain a front-line fighter. Germany continued development, basing their design on axial-flow compressors as in the Junkers 004 and the BMW 003, both being of 2000 lb thrust. By 1944, the Me262 was powered by the Junkers 004 turbojet, thus becoming Germany's and the world's first production jet fighter.

On 15 May 1941, Whittle saw success when the Gloster E28/39 made its first flight with his centrifugal-flow turbo-jet engine. Meanwhile, Halford was pressing ahead with his ideas and a contract was awarded by the Ministry of Aircraft Production for the design and development of a jet engine to be suitable for mating with a de Havilland aircraft designed for jet propulsion. The basic parameters were for an engine producing 3000 lb thrust and with a limiting diameter of 50 ins; this diameter being the minimum size to accommodate a seated pilot in the fuselage. By early 1941, the design had advanced and it had been established that the engine would be based on a ducted air intake feeding a single-sided impeller with straight-through combustion via multiple combustion chambers encircling the unit and running from the rear of the impeller casing to the forward case of the turbine. The decision to use a single-sided impeller had been influenced by the successful development of the impellers designed for the superchargers of the Gipsy Six and Napier Rapier and Dagger engines. The details were taken to Whittle for his observations. He was most interested but said he could not support the proposed design as "it did not conform". It transpired that Whittle did not want those now becoming involved with jet engines work to depart from his basic design, except with regard to size and ancillary equipment. Halford could not accept this limitation and instructed his team to continue along the lines already detailed. The radical difference in the Halford concept was the 'straight-through' gas combustion and flow. This provided continuous flow in a rearward direction and utilised the maximum availability of thrust. The Whittle design did not provide this and Halford was convinced that he could reduce aerodynamic losses by his layout. De Havilland were building the DH100 (later called the Vampire) to take this jet engine, now labelled the H1 (later called the Goblin) and much consideration was given by the engine designers to its installation in this aircraft, so the integration of engine and airframe was very much a team effort.

In this new era of power production one of the greatest problems which quickly became evident was ignorance of the combustion process, so a single chamber combustion test rig was built at one of the satellite factories. Of immediate need was a blower of sufficient capacity to feed a single combustion chamber, or 'can' as it became known. Fortunately, Napier had a large compressor which they had used to generate a 400 mph blast of air at the intakes of the Lion engine used in the Schneider Trophy seaplane. They were very co-operative and loaned it for the test rig. Even with this compressor, the air pressure obtainable was far less than that required to achieve burning at maximum fuel flow. Innumerable 'trial and error' set-ups were carried out, each trial providing further data. Useful and provable knowledge emerged and the design of the combustion head, chamber, fuel injectors and fuel pumps was developed so that they became an efficient assembly.

From this single 'can' rig, the next stage was to test at high density over the whole working range, for which a very large air-pumping plant was needed. This became available, with Ministry permission, at the site of the Dartford Tunnel, whose construction under the Thames had been halted at the outbreak of the war. This air plant had been used to pressurise the tunnel between airlocks at each end as a safety measure to keep out the river. These compressors were available, providing they remained in situ. This was fine and they could provide the quantity and pressure of air needed for full-range testing. The disadvantage was in having to send personnel and equipment across London to Dartford each day, the daily bombing raids making life even more interesting. The combustion process also required fuel-injection equipment and CAV Bosch were instrumental in providing this. The requirements for a variable-stroke pump was met by Lucas. Dowty developed the fuel system used in the Goblin Mk I and II and Lucas the pump and fuel system for the Mk III onwards. Lucas set up a combustion laboratory and de Havilland built the Gas Dynamics Laboratory at Hatfield, later re-named the Halford Laboratory, which was designed to be capable of testing all the major components of a jet engine.

The H1 design was sufficiently advanced by April 1941 to commence construction of the first engine at Stag Lane and utilising the facilities at several of the local satellite factories. These were in unexpected locations, such as the Car Mart garage and the Kemps biscuit factory on the North Circular Road. Construction of this engine was completed in 248 days from receiving the first drawings to the first test-bed start-up. This was a remarkable effort by all concerned and much credit must go to John Brodie whose organising abilities and unrelenting drive provided the recipe for successful progress.

On 2 June, the engine had its first run at top speed and the design thrust of 3000 lb was attained. At the early stages of test running a distinct note was evident at top speed, which caused concern and was traced to the compressor. Impellers were mounted in a special support and a range of vibration-inducing methods carried out. The results indicated two modes of resonance which were successfully controlled by cutting back the tips of the impeller vanes. Halford paid particular attention in design to obtain the highest possible efficiency from all components of the machine and to ensure these efficiencies were matched as a whole. A most important factor, as mismatching could create rough running, rumblings and surging at altitude, which would result in considerable discomfort for the pilot and an increase in maintenance times.

Patricia Halford joined her father in 1941 at Stag Lane working with Dr Bucher at the Propeller Division. She remained there until 1944 when she was offered a position with the Foreign Office and posted to the British Embassy in Washington, USA, as secretary to the Chief Minister and later to the Ambassador, Lord Halifax. Whilst there, she met a Lieutenant Colonel John Draper and they married in December 1946. Patricia has remained in the United States to the present time with her husband, their four children and a number of grandchildren.

In 1941, the Gas Turbine Collaboration Committee came into existence and the first meeting was held on the first of November, under the chairmanship of Dr Roxbee Cox. The interested parties were Rolls-Royce, Armstrong Siddeley, Bristol and de Havilland.

It was expected that the DH100 would be the recipient of the Goblin engines for the initial engine flight tests. Official planning had been for the Gloster F9/40, the Meteor, with two Whittle engines to be tested as the first jet fighter for the RAF. The aircraft was completed but the engines were delayed. De Havilland and Halford were contacted and asked if they could help with two Goblin engines. Engines were available but had to be modified by turning at ninety degrees so that the air ducts were horizontal and above and below the central wing spar. The installation in the DH100 required the air ducts to be vertical.

The prototype was on the tarmac at Gloster and the engines being run-up. Test pilot, Michael Daunt, walked across the front of the machine and was promptly sucked off his feet and his head and shoulders into the air intake of one engine. The throttles were immediately closed and the unfortunate pilot rescued. Fortunately, he suffered only bruising and shock. This led to the fitting of intake guards while jets were running on the ground. The first F9/40 Meteor flight was carried out with the engines rated at 2000 lb thrust, the

de Havilland Vampire   (Rolls-Royce Heritage Trust)

flight taking place from the RAF College, Cranwell on 5 March 1943 with Michael Daunt piloting.

De Havilland completed the DH100 Vampire and Geoffrey de Havilland Junior made the first flight from Hatfield in September 1943. At this stage, the engine gave 2700 lb thrust at 10,000 rpm, this being the official type approval rating. It was the first turbine to receive official approval. By the time the first flight took place, the Goblin had been subjected to 200 hours of bench testing and by the end of 1943 this had risen to 700 hours and flight data covered altitudes up to 35,000 feet at speeds nudging 500 mph. Halford was delighted at the progress of this revolutionary engine, which was giving every indication of being a reliable power source and he enthusiastically continued with development.

There were stirrings of interest from the Americans and among the visitors were members of the Lockheed Corporation who had designed a very advanced single-seater fighter, the Lockheed XP-80 Shooting Star. Halford and de Havilland received a strong request from the Ministry to help the Americans. Despite a great shortage of engines, as production had not yet got underway, two Goblins were made ready and flown out with a de Havilland engineer to California. This was in 1943. De Havilland then entered into an agreement with the Allis Chalmers Company for them to manufacture the engine under licence in the USA. The Lockheed Shooting Star, powered by the Goblin jet, first flew on 8 January 1944. At the end of the war, the Allis Chalmers contract was cancelled and the special equipment relating to the Goblin was sent to DH Canada and served to maintain Vampires for the RCAF.

Surprisingly, America had shown little interest in jet propulsion prior to 1941, although their advanced nickel alloys had contributed to improving the life of Whittle's engine and they had developed turbo-superchargers using exhaust-driven turbines, on the same principle as the one Halford had incorporated in his initial 1½-litre engine for his racing car in 1923. However, a Whittle engine had been air-lifted to the USA as early as October 1941 and, by the following year, copies had been made, two of which were installed in the Bell XP-59A fighter, the first American jet plane, first flown in October 1942. The first aircraft in both Britain and America to exceed 500 mph were powered by the DH Goblin engine. The American turbo-jet engine industry grew directly from the acquisition of two designs of British engines.

In January 1944, the Ministry of Aircraft Production formed the Gas Turbine Technical Advisory and Co-ordinating Committee. Members appointed were:-

Dr Roxbee Cox   Chairman
W E P Johnson   Secretary

The Industry Members were:-

E W Hives	Rolls-Royce
F B Halford	de Havilland
N Rowbotham	Bristol
H N Sporborg	BTH
K Baumann	Metropolitan-Vickers

To put into proportion the enormous availability of power provided by the Goblin jet engine, a few parameters illustrating its operation may be useful. Air from intakes in the leading edge of the wings is ducted to the twin intakes to the compressor. The compressor, which at maximum speed rotates at 10,000 rpm, compresses the air to 40 lb per square inch and is directed into the sixteen peripheral-mounted combustion chambers. Burners spray fuel (kerosene) into the chambers, which are designed to provide a mixing of air and fuel, and ignited. The resultant high-temperature gases are the product of this combustion (an efficiency of over ninety per cent combustion is obtained). The energy of the gases is now much increased and expands at high velocity directed through fixed guide vanes across the blades of the

The Goblin jet engine   (Rolls-Royce Heritage Trust)

117

turbine. Power developed by the turbine at full speed is in excess of 6000 horsepower. This power is transmitted by the mainshaft to the impeller. This represents the work done in compressing 100 tons of air per hour. The remaining energy in the gases is considerable and is directed into the final propelling nozzle to give 3000 lb of thrust emerging at a velocity of 1000 miles per hour.

There had been contemporary criticism of Halford's design, in particular the use of the single-sided impeller, but the subsequent operational success of the Vampire aircraft and its substantial post-war sales to European air forces proved the engine was reliable and power output was satisfactory. That the Goblin was a sought-after engine became evident in the granting of manufacturing licences to France, Italy, Sweden and Switzerland. British jet-powered aircraft did not play a significant part in the war, coming as it did at the near end of the conflict.

Halford had achieved a remarkable success with his jet engine. His unusual degree of intuition relating to power unit development and the nearly five years of unrelenting hard work by his devoted team enabled so much new ground to be covered and result in the engineering success of the Goblin. A measure of the problems encountered is shown in the development of the combustion head, where over ninety modifications were made before there was general satisfaction that high efficiency of combustion had been reached. Probably the major source of problems lay with the limitations of metallurgy at the time.

The Halford office now found that it was running new departments, including responsibility for development of the Propeller Division of de Havilland, additional premises, hiring personnel, plus many other activities far from the original remit of an engine design office, with Halford remaining an independent consultant. Although all this was done in good faith, and there was good co-operation between Halford and Geoffrey de Havilland, there were legal exposures and it was obvious there was now an uncommercial situation. The result, after close discussion, was that de Havilland proposed that the Halford organisation be taken over and absorbed into the de Havilland Aircraft Company. When this took place, Halford resigned his technical directorship of Napier. Apart from other considerations, he felt that commitments on two boards of directors would make it impossible for him to continue personal involvement with design as he would wish.

In 1944, de Havilland was re-organised and a group of companies resulted, with the Aircraft Company as group main company, controlling the Engine Company, formed in February 1944, the Propeller Company, formed in 1946 and the de Havilland Forge Company. Halford then became Chairman and Technical Director of the Engine Company.

The initial manufacture of Goblins had proceeded on a one-by-one basis as testing and development continued. By January 1943, four engines were completed, eight engines were on test by July and fourteen had been built by the end of the year. It was decided to start production of the Goblin initially at a modest five units per week as it was envisaged there would be a goodly number of production problems to be sorted out as well as trials of manufacturing methods. This led to the selection of a small factory unit at Stonegrove just north of Edgware. This recently-built factory had been specifically created to handle propeller repairs and its construction, including special propeller-balancing pits, had just been completed when priorities changed and John Brodie recruited a small team of engineers seconded from the engine design office, planning office and plant department to move to Stonegrove and lay out production lines, siting machines and establishing the support facilities that would be needed for jet engine production. By the end of 1944, it was ready to go.

As was to be expected, the production starting phase of a new engine like

The Goblin rotating assembly seen from the impeller end   (Rolls-Royce Heritage Trust)

the Goblin which differed so drastically from the usual reciprocating engine would show teething troubles. These had to be overcome as quickly as possible so that the planned expansion of output could be met.

One of the most spectacular was the machining of the impellers. A special routing machine had been commissioned from the Cincinnati Company in the USA. This machine could rout two impellers at a time, the routing tool being guided by a follower tracing the profile of a master impeller in three dimensions. Original impeller blanks were large solid 'cheeses' of RR59 magnesium material and weighed 500 lb, it not being possible to forge very much of the blade profile due to the three dimensional curve of the blades. The finished weight of a fully machined impeller was 109 lb. It was a lengthy process and the router was kept running twenty-four hours each day. Unfortunately, it emitted a loud shrieking noise, not enjoyed by the workforce and certainly did not endear the factory to the surrounding residents, the factory being sited among residential estates. However, after a few weeks, new routing tools had been designed and fitted with cutting depths and speeds adjusted so that the result was greatly improved production times and elimination of the dreaded shriek.

By kind permission of the Rolls-Royce Heritage Trust, an extract from a de Havilland report on the development of the Goblin jet engine, listing the chronological history of the development, is included as Appendix VI.

De Havilland Propellers

In June 1934, de Havilland had obtained a licence from the Hamilton Standard Corp of Hartford, USA, to build the Hamilton variable-pitch propellers. The Propeller Division grew to a successful venture from that beginning.

It was at an early stage of the war that Halford was asked to co-ordinate propeller design and development of de Havilland propellers, this enabling the essential co-relation of propellers to engines. Within two years, the business developed and contra-rotating propellers were made and supplied for the Napier Sabre and Rolls-Royce Griffon engines. Propeller projects continued to expand at a rapid rate and, by 1943, Halford had to delegate his propeller work as the pressures arising from the engine development and other projects absorbed his time and that of his team.

During 1943, Halford was involved in a serious car crash when being driven to a meeting. He suffered a fractured skull which confined him to bed for a prolonged period.

As it was now evident that the war was drawing to a close, thoughts on the direction of post-war markets in aviation had to be considered and plans established to ensure the Company's future in both military and civil fields.

Halford and de Havilland were ready to tackle the future. With the advent of commercially viable jet engines opening a new chapter in the progress of aircraft design, the aircraft designer had, for the first time in aviation history, all the engine power he wanted and an entirely new conception of air travel was a practical possibility.

Jet engine development – 1938-1945

Date of prototype	Identity	Manufacturer	Thrust lb
1938/9	Power Jets – W1A	British Thompson Houston Ltd	860
1938/9	BMW – 003	BMW (Germany)	1800
1938/40	Metro-Vickers – F2 axial-flow	Metropolitan-Vickers	2000
1939	Junkers – axial-flow	Junkers (Germany)	2200
1941	Rolls-Royce – WR1	Rolls-Royce Ltd	1450
1941/2	Power Jets W2B	Rover Motor Co Ltd	1526
1941/2	DH – H1 (Goblin)	de Havilland Engine Co Ltd	3000
1942	GEC – I-14	General Electric Co Ltd	1800
1942	Rover B26	Rover Motor Co Ltd	1450
1942	Power Jets W2/500	Rover Motor Co Ltd	1700
1943	Power Jets B23 (Welland)	Rolls-Royce Ltd	1700
1943/4	Power Jets W2/700	Power Jets	1900
1943	GEC – I-40	General Electric Co Ltd	4000
1943	RR RB37 (Derwent I)	Rolls-Royce Ltd	1900
1944	RR RB37 (Derwent V)	Rolls-Royce Ltd	3500
1944	RR Trent RB50 – turbo prop	Rolls-Royce Ltd	Prop 750hp Turb 1250lb
1944	RR RB41 – Nene	Rolls-Royce Ltd	4500
1945	DH – H2 (Ghost)	de Havilland Engine Co Ltd	4400
1945	DH Ghost – 103/48 Mk 1	de Havilland Engine Co Ltd	4850

There was an important commitment undertaken by Halford throughout the war. He was invited to become a member of the Advisory Committee to the Ministry of Aircraft Production set up by the council of the Royal Aeronautical Society at the initiative of Lord Brabazon in July 1941. Its purpose was to advise the Minister on matters of the highest secrecy related to any aspects of aeronautics with which the Minister had concern. The

Committee continued to serve successive Ministers until 1946. Initial members of the Committee were:-

Mr A H R Fedden	Bristol Aeroplane Co (Chairman)
Major T M Barlow	Fairey Aviation Co
Mr Sydney Camm	Hawker Aviation Co
Mr A Gouge	Messrs Short Brothers
Mr E W Hives	Rolls-Royce Ltd
Mr R K Pierson	Vickers Aviation
Mr C C Walker	de Havilland Aircraft Co
Capt J Lawrence Pritchard	Royal Aeronautical Society (Secretary)

Mr Hives and Major Barlow were unable to continue due to pressure of their war work and were replaced, with the Minister's approval, by:-

Major F B Halford	de Havilland Engine Co
Mr Roy Chadwick	Avro Co
Dr Leslie Aitchison	

The success of the Committee, which reported direct to the Minister, providing guidance on specific matters of development in design and production was confirmation of the wide and unique experience of its members. The Committee also brought to the Minister's attention any matter they believed should be considered as beneficial to the aviation war effort and, at the latter part of the war, their thoughts on areas which should be explored for the post-war future of aviation in this country. An assessment of engine design covering both World War I and II indicated that engine power output was increased by about three times in each war.

CHAPTER TEN

1946 – 1955 Post-war developments
Gipsy series, jets, turboprops and rockets

On the completion of the war in Europe and with the Allies exercising control in Germany, the opportunity to extend the testing of the Goblin jet became available by using the BMW altitude test cell at Munich. This cell was twelve feet in diameter and could be evacuated to create altitude conditions applicable at 50,000 feet. In addition, intake air could be controlled from very low speed up to 550 mph and temperatures brought down to minus 70 degrees Centigrade.

Dr David Cockburn (Halford's Chief Aerodynamics Engineer and a compressor specialist) was sent to Munich to examine and report on this facility. His findings were very positive, a series of tests were planned and a Goblin engine was shipped out and installed in the unit. There followed seven hundred hours of testing, completed in a few weeks, which provided information flight testing could not have achieved.

The use of a static assembly enabled the engine to be laboratory instrumented and infinitely variable conditions could be applied and the performance recorded. The very extensive amount of testing to which the engine was subjected established not only performance but also reliability, so this testing provided a most necessary basis for offering this type of power unit for civil aircraft use and the extensive flying hours to be expected when operating an airline service.

Immediately following the end of the war, the RAF was to be re-equipped and so, even after five years of unrelenting pressure of work to meet the needs of the conflict in the air, there was no opportunity for any relaxation of effort in the design office. It was as early as 1943 that Halford started an assessment of engine requirements for the future in close co-operation with the de Havilland aircraft designers and sales departments. The assessment began with a review of the Gipsy engine range and initiated various updates, particularly to adapt for variable-pitch propellers and to meet the training requirements of the RAF. The initial step was to increase the previous 118mm bore/140mm stroke to 120mm bore/150mm stroke to pave the way for the increase of horsepower that would be in demand. Both four- and six-cylinder engines were based on these sizes so that many components were interchangeable on all ranges. In the demand for higher power, supercharged versions of both four and six-cylinder were to be available with direct or geared drive, and to take controllable-pitch propellers. The six-cylinder engines would be able to take the new de Havilland constant-speed, feathering and braking propeller. Four-cylinder units would take the new de Havilland manually-operated propeller.

The engine first to be uprated, the normally aspirated 160 hp Gipsy Major 30, was now fitted with a supercharger and became the 200 hp Gipsy Major 50. Next, the six-cylinder Gipsy Queen 30 replaced the Gipsy Queen III and the Gipsy Queen 50 was the supercharged version of 295 hp, followed by the Gipsy Queen 70 – a geared version of the 50. Over the next two years, the various Gipsy engine types were thinned out and the Major 31 and 51 with the Gipsy Queen 71 continued in production.

Late 1945 was the year which saw a pair of Gipsy Queen 71s fitted to the DH104 Dove, a most attractive low-wing monoplane. The smooth and vibration-free performance of this machine was outstanding, due largely to the supercharged, geared six-cylinder engine with Dr Kerr Wilson's vibration dampers fitted to the crankshaft webs in conjunction with the three-bladed adjustable-pitch propellers. On a flight to the Channel Isles, Halford took great delight in balancing a coin on its edge to demonstrate the smoothness of his engines. This new de Havilland aircraft became highly successful and orders flooded in from around the world.

The success of the Gipsy Queen 71, the highest-powered post-war Gipsy piston engine rated 330 bhp at 2800 rpm for take-off, was the result of considerable development work. The problems created with six-cylinder engines, where the effort to design for a small frontal area suitable for wing installation with minimum disruption to air flow, resulted in a comparatively

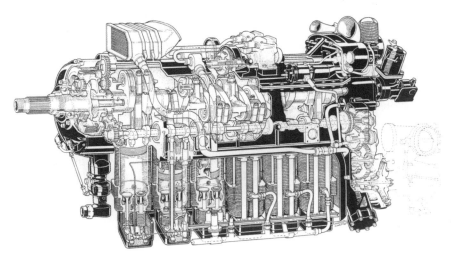

Gipsy Queen 71 330bhp, 1945   (Lyndon Jones)

long narrow structure. The overall dimensions were:-

Length   1787.75mm (70.38 inches)
Width   394.00mm (15.52 inches)
Depth   847.75mm (33.38 inches)

The long crankshaft did contribute to the generation of torsional vibration, a subject of which little was known in the 1930s, but much had been learnt during the war years. Dr Kerr Wilson's studies into this area produced his successful pendulum-type dampers.

As the Gipsy Queen 71 was supercharged and geared, there was concern that the stress on the front end of the crankshaft and propeller drive shaft could be excessive. To overcome this, with the propeller reduction gear being a simple epicyclic gear and coupled to the propeller with a Bibby spring-type coupling, the rear-mounted supercharger was driven, by a quill shaft of some flexibility, from the planetary gears and passed through the hollow camshaft to the supercharger impeller gears. This shaft also drove the fuel control unit and the tachometer. By this means, any torsional stress to the camshaft was avoided. A second quill shaft, within the top cover, also connected to the planetary gears, providing the drive for the magnetos, air compressor, vacuum pump and electric generator. The introduction of the Bibby-type spring coupling, extensively used in many applications, was a simple and highly effective means of preventing shock loads. Smoother running was also assisted by keeping to the revised firing order of 1.2.4.6.5.3. This was confirmed during discussions with the RAE on the problems of torsional vibration and, despite requiring changes to the inlet manifold and carburettor positioning, it did prove to be an effective solution.

In mid-December 1945, an exhibition of the Gipsy engine range was mounted at the Mayfair Hotel in central London at which potential buyers were entertained. A useful assessment of the possible demand resulted and certainly assisted forward production planning. The post-war market for engines began to look very promising. The success of the Dove boosted the production of the Gipsy Queen 71 and British and foreign orders created a steady demand. In September 1945, the Engine Company published a handbook entitled, de Havilland Gipsy Engines Series 30, 50 and 70 – Preliminary Statement. This gave the basic parameters of the engines available for the post-war market. It also set the 'family tree' of the Gipsy range from the beginning. This appeared as follows:-

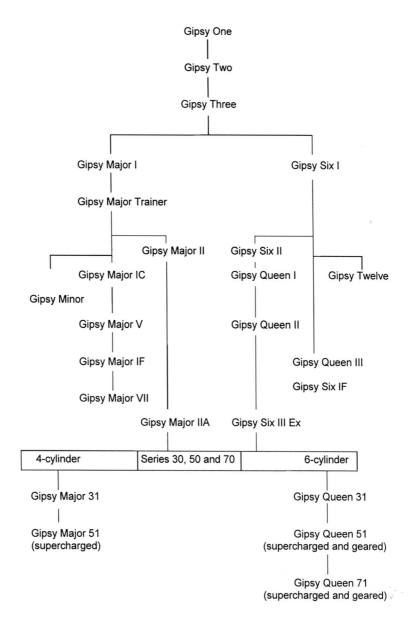

In May 1946, Halford presented a lecture to the Royal Society of Arts entitled, 'Jet Propulsion' in which he outlined the use of jets for long-distance passenger flights. His prognosis was based on a four-engine aircraft, each engine providing 15,000 lb thrust. These would be axial-flow units, that is with multi-disc impellers and multi-stage turbine discs. This lecture gave much food for thought in the aircraft design and operating industries, as it laid down some parameters for the direction which future development could take.

As an initial venture into the development of small gas turbines, Halford pursued the use of the turboprop engine. To this end, he designed the H3 with the idea of replacing the Gipsy Queens in a pressurised version of the Dove aircraft. The H3 had a two-stage centrifugal compressor coupled to a three-stage turbine with a reduction gearing to the propeller. This engine was built in 1946/7 and the single unit had had only limited running on the test-bed when the Government withdrew its support for small jet development. De Havilland was not the only company to have to terminate this particular area of development.

The next generation of the Goblin-type unit was well advanced in design as a 4800 lb-thrust unit named the Ghost Mk 1. It started bench testing in 1945 for Service use in the DH112 Venom. In 1946, it became a priority to prepare the Ghost for civil use to power the DH106 Comet which de Havilland were pressing ahead to get into service as the first jet-engined airliner in the world. There was considerable competition to be first in this race. To jump ahead to 1948, de Havilland were able to add to their successes in world records when, on 23 March 1948, John Cunningham in a Ghost-powered Vampire took the world altitude record at 59,492 feet. This was shortly followed by John Derry establishing a new international closed circuit speed record at 605 mph in the swept-wing tail-less Goblin-powered DH108 on 12 April.

As the Ghost had been specifically designed for military use the design now required reviewing to provide those essential parameters for civil airline operation – that is reliability, safety and longevity. Not that these were lacking in the military version, but the prospect of the greatly increased flying hours needed by an airline running regular schedules called for re-thinking throughout the design and this entailed amendments to a large percentage of the engine. Undertaking this programme resulted in the expenditure of many thousands of hours of bench testing plus 5200 hours of flight testing. The flights were carried out using a modified Lancastrian and later moving to the prototype Comet. The development programme extended over a five-year period and benefited from the input of those on Halford's staff whose pre-war experience of design, development and maintenance of aero-engines in civil use was invaluable in setting the base line for future civil power units.

The future did indeed have a great and painful blow to deliver to de Havilland when, in 1954, two Comet airliners met with disaster, throwing a long shadow over commercial jet operations. The engines of the crashed airliners were recovered by the remarkable skill of the Royal Navy and subjected to the most detailed examination by the Aircraft Investigation Department of the RAE. It finally emerged that no fault was found and the work of jet development continued. At the time of the loss of the two Comets, the Ghost engine had in fact become so reliable that it was achieving almost 1000 hours between overhauls.

Halford said it had taken him twenty-two years improving piston engines to produce an aero-engine attaining 1000 hours between overhauls (the Gipsy Major), but he was able to achieve 1000 hours between overhauls with the Goblin and Ghost jets within eight years. The Ghost gave 5000 lb static

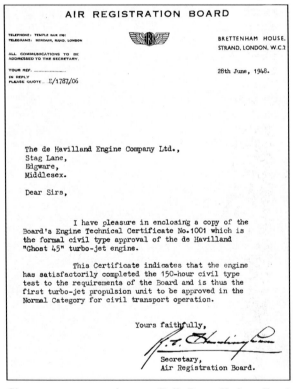

Ghost type test approval (Rolls-Royce Heritage Trust)

DH106 Comet airliner with Ghost jet engines   (Author)

thrust. It would require a propeller engine of 12,000 hp to provide the same thrust at the propeller, due to propeller efficiency of about 53%.

In 1949, de Havilland Engine Co were able to publish an advertisement for their jet engines as follows:-

April 1944	First jet engine to exceed 500 mph in both Britain and America
January 1945	First jet engine to obtain Military Type Approval
March 1948	World's altitude record for aeroplanes – 59,446 ft (18119 metres)
April 1948	World's speed record for 100 km closed circuit – 605.23 mph
July 1948	First jet engine to make Atlantic crossing
July 1948	First jet engine to obtain approval for civil passenger services
August 1948	Successful completion of severest-ever 500-hour engine test

In the early 1950s, an agreement had been made with the General Electric Company of the United States for the exchange of technical information relating to gas turbines. This became a very successful area for both companies. Of particular interest, and subject to joint development, were the variable-incidence blading, developed and used by General Electric,

Return of the Royal Flight around Europe in the DH Comet, 23 May 1952. FBH talks with HRH The Princess Margaret and Queen Elizabeth with F T Hearle of de Havilland
(Patricia Draper)

reduction gearing improvements, variable nozzles and re-heat systems for afterburning.

It was as early as 1950 that Halford considered the possibilities and implications of supersonic flight and the power units which would be required. He focused on two concepts:-

1. The design of a large-thrust jet engine
2. The combination of a smaller lightweight jet, together with a controllable liquid-fuelled rocket engine.

A series of design studies were inaugurated and Concept 1 emerged as a comparatively low-pressure, axial-flow compressor engine. The low pressure was possible because of the considerable ram effect which would be available at supersonic speeds. The design envisaged small frontal area and an axial-flow compressor with reduced stages of blading. This was in an effort to overcome having a large number of small compressor blades, which were then vulnerable in service and costly to manufacture. His initial proposal was for an axial-flow jet to give static thrust of 12,000 lb at 800 degrees C with take-off thrust of 15,000 lb at 1000 degrees C. The estimated engine weight of 6000 lb and an external diameter of five feet with a length of 17 feet were the basic limitations. It was expected that development would raise the thrust to 20,000 lb and this was allowed for the design. This was a private venture by de Havilland with no official support.

A unit was built and named the Gyron; it first ran in January 1953, reaching 15,000 lb thrust. By September, official approval was received for experimental flight. The Ministry of Supply issued a contract for continuing development and the manufacture of additional units. A Sperrin aircraft was adapted by Short and Harland in Belfast as a flying test-bed and flight testing started in September 1955. Official type-test approval had now been given. Continuing bench testing and development had pushed the dry thrust up to 20,000 lb and to over 30,000 lb with re-heat. In early 1956, a Mark II version with an additional stage of compressor blades again raised the dry thrust up to 25,000 lb and to over 29,000 lb with re-heat. However, no aircraft was available for the Gyron at the time. Development had continued as a private de Havilland venture. Sir Sydney Camm designed a Hawker fighter, the P1121, using the Gyron and built one as a company venture, though it was not completed.

The foreseen need of 1000-hp units for light aircraft and helicopters was discussed in some detail and this led to projects being initiated by both de Havilland and General Electric. However, there was no official support for the de Havilland project, the General Electric T58 being selected for future development.

The Sprite and Super Sprite

As work continued on the Gipsy series of piston engines and the Goblin/Ghost jets, Halford also considered the possibilities of rocket power, remembering that the Germans had made progress before and during the war years with rocket-propelled units. Dr Johannes Winkler, a founder member of the German Rocket Society in 1927, was, in 1929, commissioned by Junkers to undertake experiments on rocket-assisted take-off for seaplanes and German development in rocket units continued.

Halford formed a team of four engineers in 1946 led by ex-propeller specialist, A V Cleaver, to investigate rocket propulsion. They were able to study documents obtained from German sources now available at the RAE and also at the government Rocket Propulsion Establishment. The attraction of rocket power was the rating of thrust per unit of weight, the small size, the thrust being almost independent of altitude, improving slightly with height, an opposite fact to air-consuming engines. With units of high consumption and short duration application for assisted take-off was a logical development.

In 1947, while using a Lancastrian as a flying test-bed for the Ghost engine, the opportunity to experience assisted take-off using a German Walter 109/500 rocket unit gave measurable data and, by 1948, design had started on the Sprite assisted take-off engine to give 5000 lb thrust for sixteen seconds using high test peroxide (HTP). This was fed from a pressure tank into a chamber which was contained in a further pressure vessel filled with calcium permanganate. Both HTP and calcium permanganate were mixed in the combustion chamber and produced steam at 600 degrees C as a propulsion jet. By November 1949, the Sprite was running on the test-bed. The initial idea was to use this engine to provide assisted take-off for the Comet airliner under tropical conditions. Flight tests with the Comet began in mid 1951 and ran until the end of 1952, during which time there were over 200 trial firings. However, the additional thrust obtained with water injection in the Ghost engines proved more than adequate for the Comet, so the Sprite was not used on this aircraft.

By now, the Ministry were sufficiently interested to place a development contract enabling eight Sprites to be built and, in addition to test-bed firings, some thirty take-offs fitted to the Comet were made. This developed into the Super Sprite, first running by the Spring of 1953. The Super Sprite used kerosene injection which, with the cooling of the combustion chamber throat, gave 4200 lb thrust for forty seconds. Two units were fitted to the Vickers Valiant bomber. The Super Sprite became the first rocket engine to receive Air Ministry Type Approval by September 1954. Production started and some one hundred and sixty were made. In parallel with the development programme on the Super Sprite, Halford initiated his Concept 2 for the combination of a smaller, lightweight turbo-jet engine with controllable liquid-fuelled rocket engine. (Details of de Havilland's rocket development can be found in the RAeS Journal of February 1951 under the title *Rockets and Assisted Take-Off* – a lecture given by A V Cleaver, Special Projects Engineer, the de Havilland Engine Company).

On a personal note, the year 1950 saw Halford take office as vice-president of the Royal Aeronautical Society and in the following year elected to president to hold the office until the end of 1952. During his presidency in 1951, the Society were hosts of the Anglo-American Aeronautical Conference. The inaugural cocktail party was held at Brighton and Halford undertook the responsibility of ensuring that this would be a success and devoted his energies to that end. It was not known to anyone that he had just received confirmation that day he was suffering from cancer to the throat. He carried on with no hint of his personal concerns and continued to carry the party, and later the Conference, through to acclaim. He later underwent surgery and quietly fought a courageous battle for two years, finally conquering it.

It is necessary, at this point, to record the Government's policies for the immediate needs of the Air Arm which led to the issue of Air Staff Requirement OR301 in August 1951. This set out the need for a high-speed rocket-propelled interceptor fighter and was followed by an amended version (OR301 Issue 2) which resulted in the issue of Specification F124T in January 1952. This specification for the fighter was based on the development by both Armstrong Siddeley Motors Ltd and de Havilland Engine Co Ltd of 2000 lb thrust rocket motors. The concept, being based on the German Me163, was for a rocket-powered take-off and climb to 100,000 feet to intercept a supersonic bomber and then making a single attack before all the rocket fuel was expended, followed by a gliding return to earth.

Companies interested in this project were Blackburn & General Aircraft Co Ltd, Bristol Aeroplane Co Ltd, Short Brothers & Harland Ltd and Saunders Roe Ltd. The specification was amended to include a small conventional turbo-jet when it was realised the rocket motor would not provide the necessary electrical power.

Saunders Roe submitted their proposal to the Air Ministry based on this specification, but were not happy that this was the best solution so they proposed an addendum for a different aircraft of a more conventional type which would have a better performance and capable of rapid refuelling and rearming. Their proposal was successful and a new Specification F138D was issued in June 1953 followed in October by a contract for the construction of three of the prototype, the SR53, which would be fitted with both an Armstrong Siddeley Viper turbo-jet and a de Havilland Spectre rocket motor.

A new design for an enlarged aircraft (Project P177) was started based on using a de Havilland Gyron Junior engine and the Spectre rocket motor. This was planned for flight in mid 1957. To provide a lightweight jet engine to be used in conjunction with the Spectre, the Gyron Junior was designed as an engine one-third smaller than the Gyron. The Spectre rocket engine operated on hydrogen peroxide with kerosene and was controllable between 1000 and 8000 lb thrust. Because of the expectations of the P177, and to protect their interests, de Havilland acquired a substantial interest in Saunders Roe Ltd in 1956.

On 16 April 1955, at his home *Monkbarns*, Frank Halford suddenly died of a coronary thrombosis. At only sixty-one years of age, this sudden and entirely unexpected end to a gifted life was a shattering blow not only to his family but to all in his team and the myriads of friends in the aircraft industry world-wide.

Halford never saw the Gyron Junior run as this did not happen until four months after his death. Flight tests of the SR53 provided valuable data, but the SR53 remained a research aircraft. The Spectre/Gyron Junior combination was first tried in an adapted Canberra used as a flying test-bed. Following this, the Air Ministry placed an order for nine Saunders Roe P177 in September 1956. Large production orders were expected with the possibility of substantial orders from West Germany and, in November, the Ministry of Supply approved the granting of a manufacturing license to the Germans. The market was looking very promising until the publication of the Defence White Paper in April 1957. Prior to the issue of this policy document, the effects of Government indecision on whether to replace manned military aircraft with missiles had delayed the placing of orders for supersonic aircraft and was causing increased concern in the industry. The policy requirements of the White Paper, when it finally was issued, directed that the major part of development work on air defence was to be centred on missiles. The exception was the continuing development of the English Electric P1 fighter. However, the Gyron Junior did find an application for a new naval strike aircraft, the Blackburn NA39 Buccaneer which first flew in April 1958, three years after Halford's death.

Following the end of the war, it was necessary to take stock of the scattered collection of factories and satellite production units which had been hastily set up for the needs of the war. It was certain that the pre-war plans to re-develop Stag Lane site by the local borough for housing, as had happened to the old aerodrome area in the thirties, would be regenerated. De Havilland looked for a suitable new site for the Engine Company. Their choice fell on Leavesden, at which they already had manufacturing facilities.

Leavesden, a small village situated between Watford and Abotts Langley, included 117 acres of land purchased in 1937 by the Borough of Watford for recreational purposes and named the King George V Recreational Grounds. By the later part of 1940, the need to increase bomber production led to the Ministry of Aircraft Production requiring de Havilland to undertake the construction of the Vickers Wellington. This meant that a new factory would be needed and aerial surveys to identify suitable sites showed the King George V Recreation Grounds offered the major assets needed for the manufacture of aircraft. The terrain was flat and suitable for a runway, also it was adjacent to the good roads necessary to bring in supplies and the local population was a good catchment for labour. The Air Ministry obtained possession for the MAP by means of a compulsory purchase order and construction of two factories, together with a 150-foot wide, 1000-yard-long runway commenced immediately. De Havilland occupied No 2 factory but the initial intention of de Havilland manufacturing Wellingtons was changed to the production of the Mosquito, as the demand for this aircraft made increased production urgent. However, this de Havilland involvement at Leavesden did not include engine manufacture until the London Aircraft

Production Group (the aircraft manufacturing activity of London Transport) ceased using it in 1945. Thus the large facilities of No 1 factory became available whilst de Havilland was still active in No 2 factory. Negotiations between de Havilland, the Ministry and Watford Borough Council resulted in the company establishing post-war manufacture for engines at Leavesden. The initial transfer of Engine Company activities commenced with the installation of the work from those shadow factories around the Edgware district followed, in the late 1950s, by jet engine production from Stonegrove. Piston engine production was to continue for some years at Stag Lane and it was not until 1967 that the design and development departments moved together with the engine manufacture.

The Halford Laboratory

With the advent of the powerful Gyron engine, examining the problem of providing sophisticated testing facilities showed that the existing facilities as developed for the Ghost and Goblin engines would fall far short of the new requirements. To this end, de Havilland – who had invested a very large amount of money to meet future needs in 1947 – built the Gas Dynamics Laboratory in Hatfield initially for combustion research. Later, in 1952, the laboratory was greatly extended and, in honour of the man who inspired it all, was renamed The Halford Laboratory.

It was a measure of Halford's foresight that he created a massive 18,000 horsepower compressor test rig powered by four Ghost engines of 5000 lb thrust each. The outlets of the jets were paired and each pair provided the drive to one of two large industrial turbines. It was created to test the Gyron engine and thanks to Halford's appreciation of the future increase that would emerge in gas turbine power requirements, it was able to continue handling engines up to the late 1970s including products from Bristol and Rolls-Royce. The Laboratory also expanded its facilities to keep pace with rocket and missile development testing.

Non-aircraft jets

In 1947, Halford was able to assist Sir Malcolm Campbell who had decided to undertake another attempt on the world water speed record. He was looking for an engine to give the power needed to break the existing record, which he had established at 141.74 mph. Campbell wanted to use a Goblin engine. A new boat, the *Bluebird K3*, was under construction at the Vosper yard in Portsmouth. With permission from the Air Ministry, de Havilland were prepared to loan a Goblin for the attempt.

In early 1947, an engine was modified and underwent tests on the test-bed

Patricia sees FBH off from the USA on liner, Isle de France, returning to the UK in the late
1950s (Patricia Draper)

FBH presides at the RAeS's third Anglo-American Aeronautical Conference, Brighton,
3-7 September 1951. (Ann Spring)
FBH, Mrs Richardson, Mayor of Brighton Alderman Eric Simms, Lady Mayoress Mrs
Simms, Mrs Halford, Admiral Richardson

at Hatfield. It was transported to Vospers for installation. By mid July, the boat was ready and taken to Coniston Water. Campbell took a practice run but, after a short distance, returned to report that on reaching a 100 mph the boat veered uncontrollably at right angles and did not respond to the steering. The craft was returned to Vospers for tests and modifications to the hull. By mid July, further tests were carried out in Poole Harbour. The boat then returned to Coniston Water in early August. At the time, Campbell – at 62 years of age – was a sick man. He took the boat out on test and found that at 120 mph it suffered severe porpoising, the bow pounding up and down. No reason was found for this problem. The engine was running perfectly. Campbell had to review the situation. He decided to abandon the attempt as, with no progress in identifying the cause of the troubles and with mounting costs plus his own health problems, it was the wisest course. This proved to be Campbell's last record attempt and it was on 31 December 1948 he died.

In 1952, another Brooklands friend contacted Halford on a similar mission. John Cobb considered using a Ghost engine in his proposed speed boat, Crusader, to make an attempt on the world water speed record. He sought the help of Halford and the de Havilland Engine Company. This help was forthcoming and an engine was modified and fitted. Cobb took the boat to Loch Ness and, on 29 September 1952, he started out on his record run. All went well until he reached 240 mph when the boat broke up and Cobb was killed. A plaque set into a stone plinth at the side of the Loch remains as a memorial to a great racing friend.

CHAPTER ELEVEN

Final honours

Frank Halford's design career, which spanned the years from 1915 to 1955, produced some fifty-seven engines which saw service in both civil and military aviation. Undoubtedly, the pressing need for a high-power engine for the RFC in WW1, which directed Halford's secondment to Beardmore, was the start of his design career. Probably the two factors which had the greatest influence on his approach to engine design was the 1914-18 Hispano-Suiza aero-engine and his post WW1 close association with Sir Harry Ricardo.

Progressive designs produced their engineering problems, some of which stretched the metallurgists to find improved high-tensile and chrome-alloy steels and magnesium alloys. Manufacturing practices were always under review.

It is a maxim of design work that the most difficult thing to achieve is simplicity. Halford achieved this with his Cirrus, Gipsy and gas turbine series of engines. This cannot be said, however, for his H-section Napier units. His concept of arranging four in-line units of four and six cylinders on a common crankcase and coupled twin crankshafts plus, in the case of the Sabre engine, the use of single-sleeve valves, departed from his other designs and were complex units.

These designs provided the large horsepower units required, but to do so absorbed a very large amount of design effort. There were some who, at the time and later with hindsight, have been critical. Servicing such complex engines in wartime operational conditions did not earn the approbation of ground crews. However, they provided the power needed for high-speed aircraft which were most successful in air-to-air combat and ground-attack operations. The Sabre was the most powerful piston engine in the world at that time. Later, his determination to stay with the single-sided impeller for the Goblin jet engine and to develop the Ghost on the same basic design paid off in meeting wartime needs and was available for the immediate post-war market.

From the time he started his consultancy, he steadily built up a reputation for designing engines for de Havilland which could be manufactured with economy and this, plus their sturdy reliability in service and with simple maintenance, ensured world-wide sales for the de Havilland organisation. This was reflected by the purchase of his business by de Havilland in 1943 and the creation of the de Havilland Engine Company Ltd as a separate entity with Halford at the head. In addition, he was entrusted with the development and expansion of the de Havilland Propeller Company.

Thirty-four years after his death, the design director of Aircraft for de Havilland, Mr R E Bishop, was asked about his relationship with Frank Halford. The questioner had in mind the stressful period between the Aircraft and Engine companies at the time of the Comet airliner disasters. R E Bishop had expressed his preference for the Rolls-Royce axial-flow Avon engines for the Comet in place of the Ghost, but Halford's jets had produced, under wartime pressures, a reliable engine and Halford's decision to base the Goblin design on a centrifugal single-sided compressor and single-disc turbine, as in the Whittle engine, was determined by his experience of centrifugal superchargers and wartime urgency required practical progress in as short a time as possible. Bishop's response to the question was in fulsome praise of his long time friend and he said, *"Frank Halford has never been given the credit he deserves. He was the first man to make a practical jet engine. Whittle never did that. Halford was also the first man to make a passenger jet engine"*. Whether this comment is accepted, nevertheless, it is a fact that Halford's Goblin engine was the first to fly in a production British jet fighter, the Gloster Meteor, and later the DH Vampire and the first to fly in a production American jet fighter.

In a letter to the Royal Commission supporting the idea of an award to Sir Frank Whittle, Dr Roxbee Cox wrote, *"Rolls-Royce is achieving success with engines which are a direct descendant of the Whittle engine and de Havilland is achieving its contribution with an engine which would not have been designed but for the stimulus and information provided by the early Whittle successes"*. The success of the Goblin brought the further success of the more powerful Ghost so that, as the war ended and the difficult post-war period began, the de Havilland organisation had available two well tried and commercially viable jet engines. That Halford was aware of the limitations of his initial jet designs became evident when he presented his 1946 Royal Society of Arts lecture in which he advocated axial-flow designs for his perception of the future power units for long-distance air travel.

Aside from his aero-engine design work, he had enjoyed a passionate involvement in racing, first with motorcycles and then with cars. He became a member of the BARC (Brooklands Automobile Racing Club) in 1923. He eventually withdrew from active participation in 1934, claiming financial reasons, but the sport provided an outlet for his competitive spirit and, at the same time, involved the engineer, as his advanced Halford Special car clearly indicated.

Halford was a unique product of the age of petrol power. Right from his school days, he showed an uncanny affinity with, and knowledge of, the internal combustion engine. He developed with the engines he produced and continued in the forefront of the field for his entire life. His name appears on over eighty patents from 1944 to 1959. All are related to the internal combustion engine. His service in the RFC and the RAF contributed greatly to improvements in performance and reliability of the aero-engines of that first World War period. His efforts at Napiers enabled the company to remain viable. His designs of light aero-engines from the early twenties until his death ensured the success of de Havilland aircraft which continued into the gas turbine engine era followed by rocket power for assisted take-off. A total of over 27,600 Gipsy engines was produced by de Havilland and stand witness to the success of a design, the model of simplicity, reliability and economy.

He was blessed with a great and remarkable talent, was able to convey this to others and get their enthusiastic support. He served his country in two world wars and in the years between and after, helped put the British aviation industry in a powerful position world-wide. Let the words of his long-time friend and associate, John Brodie, be the fitting eulogy to Frank Bernard Halford:-

"A great person is lost to the world of aero-engine designers and engineers. His active brain was never still, always stretching out for more power, for high efficiencies, for new developments. Throughout the years, he never outstripped his own strength. Each increasing growth in his

Daughter, Patricia Draper, receives postumous award of the Elmer A Sperry Medal in recognition of her father's development of the Ghost jet engine at Plaza Hotel, New York, 1959.　　　　　　　　　　　　　　　　　　　　　　　　　　　(Patricia Draper)
Seated left: Dr Eric Moult. Seated right: Sir A Burke and Mr Buckingham

organisation was taken with assurance and matched to his forward vision. It grew throughout and never to my knowledge suffered a recession.

Probably his most outstanding characteristic was his amazing forethought as to what the aircraft industry would need as engines in the years ahead. Surely, there is no single man in all the world of aviation who has left his personal signature on aero-engine design so clearly over such a long period."

These words capture exactly the whole essence of the man and to those who were privileged to be part of the organisation he created, the feeling was one of being part of an engineering family and not just an employee of a business. Such was the atmosphere of Frank Halford's design office. After his untimely death, it tried – as everyone did – to continue in the same spirit, but it was not the same. Certainly, it never would be the same, although everybody did more than their best. The resulting future, however, would have drawn no adverse comments from his spirit.

He became a Fellow of the Royal Aeronautical Society in 1927 and in 1935 was awarded the Society's Silver Medal for his work on both the Cirrus and Gipsy series of engines. In appreciation of his vision in jet engine development, following the delivery of his paper 'Jet Propulsion' on 1 May 1946, he was presented by the Royal Society of Arts with its Silver Medal. In the 1948 New Year's Honours, he was appointed a Commander of the Order of the British Empire. In 1949, he was elected to the Council of the Royal Aeronautical Society and, in 1950, further recognition by the Royal Aeronautical Society was given by the presentation of the British Gold Medal for Achievements in Aeronautics. He was elected vice-president of the Royal Aeronautical Society in 1950 and president during 1951/52.

Eminence in his profession, confirmed by the awards he received, would have given rise to the expectation of a knighthood in parallel with many of his contemporaries in aviation development. However, this was not to be, possibly because of his divorce. Now forty years later, there is more tolerance in these circumstances. Following his death in 1955, recognition of his talents by the international aviation community came four years later with the posthumous award of the Elmer A Sperry Medal for the development of the Ghost gas turbine engine. His daughter, Patricia, accepted the medal on behalf of the family at a special dinner at the Plaza Hotel, New York, in 1959.

The de Havilland Company inaugurated the annual de Havilland Scholarship for the benefit of boys at his old school, Felsted (see Appendix IX).

The Royal Aeronautical Society created the Halford Memorial Lectures, the first of which was given by John Brodie on 5 February 1959 at the

Hatfield Technical College as a lasting tribute to his friend of so many years. These lectures have continued over the years and are recorded in Appendix VIII.

A memorial service was held at Christ Church in Dover Street, London, adjacent to the Royal Aeronautical Society headquarters on Thursday 5 May 1955 at 11.30am. It was attended by very many of his friends and associates in aviation in support of his family in their sudden loss. Following his death, his daughter received his treasured racing trophies. These were all lost, with other valuables, in a burglary at her home in the United States and were never recovered. Patricia's mother eventually joined her daughter and family in the United States where she lived to reach the admirable age of ninety-seven. His mother, Ethel, outlived her son, continuing in the family home at Edwalton until her death in 1958.

Halford's greatest memorial will be his engines, each design providing the needs of the aviation market be it civil or military. Outstanding as the products of a great British engineer.

APPENDIX I

People and Companies

Various people and companies who played a significant part throughout Halford's career have received mention in the foregoing chapters, plus those whose involvement in aviation, particularly in its early days and during the First World War, were to affect Halford's future albeit by policy decisions at Government or military levels.

It may prove of interest to those readers who are not so ancient as the author, to have available a very brief synopsis of those individuals and the positions they held plus a similar summary of companies whose operations had a bearing, directly or peripherally, on Halford's career.

People

ARSCOTT, W H, Bsc

1926	Joined Halford as design draughtsman.
1934	Chief Designer – seconded to the Aero-engine Section of D Napier & Son Ltd.
1944	Chief Designer – de Havilland Engine Co Ltd.

BAGNALL-WILD, R K, Brigadier General CMG, CBE, DL, JP – born 1878

1893	Commissioned in the Royal Engineers.
1919-21	Director of Aeronautical Inspection – Air Ministry
1921-24	Director of Research – Air Ministry
	Past President of the Royal Aeronautical Society and of the Institute of Automobile Engineers.

BANKS, Air Commodore Francis Rodwell, CB, OBE, FRAeS, MIAE, FInstPT, MSAE 1898-1985

1914	Engineering apprenticeship and joined the RNVR on anti-submarine patrol.
1918	Commanded high-speed surface craft.
1919	Transported six such vessels to Russia by rail. After demobilisation worked on diesel engine development.
1924	Started aero-engine career testing large airship engines for the Air Ministry.

1927	Chief Experimental Engineer to Peter Hooker Ltd at Walthamstow, known as the British Gnome and Le Rhone Engine Company.
1929	Joined the Anglo-American Oil Company as technical head of the Ethyl Export Corporation specialising in the development of leaded fuels and special fuels for competitive work, particularly the Schneider Trophy and motor speed trials in America requiring frequent visits to America and Europe.
1939	Joined the RAFVR and obtained wings at Upavon. Later seconded to the Ministry of Aircraft Production as Director of Aero-engine Production.
1945	Appointed Director General of Aero-engine Production.
1946	Rejoined Associated Ethyl Company.
1952	Director of Aero-engine Research and Development – MoS.
1954-59	Director of Bristol Aeroplane Company.
1969	President of the RAeS.

BARING, Wing Commander The Hon Maurice, OBE, Chevalier of the Legion of Honour 1874-1945

1898	Entered Diplomatic Service – Attaché to Paris.
1900	Attaché in Copenhagen.
1902	Third Secretary in Rome.
1903-4	Foreign Office (resigned 1904).
1904-9	War correspondent to the Morning Post.
1914	Served in the RFC as ADC to Gen Sir David Henderson with the rank of Major, served in the RAF on its formation.
1915-18	ADC to Sir Hugh Trenchard.

BISHOP, R E, CBE, FRAeS

1921	Joined de Havilland Aircraft Co Ltd as apprentice.
1936	In charge of drawing office.
1940	Design Director, de Havilland Aircraft Co Ltd Responsible for the design of the Mosquito.
1946	Received CBE.
1949	Led the design team of the Comet airliner.
1952	Deputy Managing Director – de Havilland Aircraft Co Ltd and Director of the de Havilland Propeller Co Ltd. Member of the Technical Executive Committee and Technical Board of the Society of British Aircraft Constructors.

BROAD, Capt Hubert Stanford, MBE, AFC – born 1897

1915	Learnt to fly at Hendon – served with RNAS.
1918	Transferred to RAF.
1921-35	Chief test pilot for de Havilland.
1935-39	Served in RAF.
1939-40	Seconded to RAE Farnborough.
1941-47	Chief production test pilot for Hawker Aircraft Co Ltd.

BRODIE, John Longmuir Penman, MIMechE, FRAeS, Hon MSLAE 1899-1959

1914	Apprenticeship with Arrol-Johnston, Dumfries.
1923	Joined Halford as draughtsman, was first employee.
1928	Chief draughtsman to Halford.
1935	Assistant chief designer to Halford.
1944	Engineering manager – de Havilland Engine Co Ltd and Propeller Division then Engineering Director of the de Havilland Engine Co Ltd.

BULMAN, Major George Purvis, CBE, BSc, MIAS, FRAeS – born Egypt 1892

1914-18	Served in RFC.
1915	Assistant Inspector of Engines – AID.
1918-21	Seconded to Ministry of Munitions as Deputy Chief Inspector (Engines).
1928	Assistant Director of R&D (Engines) Air Ministry.
1929	Deputy Director of R&D (Engines).
1939-41	Director of Engine Development and Director of Engine Production.
1944	Director of Construction of Research Facilities.
1950-52	President of the RAeS.

CAMM, Sir Sidney Hon FRAeS, CBE – 1893-1966

1918	Joined Martinsyde as Mechanic.
1922	Left Martinsyde to join Mr Handasyde.
1923	Joined Hawker Engineering Co as designer on the Cygnet I & II light aircraft.
1925	Chief Designer – Hawker Aircraft.
1935	Appointed to the Board.

1950-51	Vice-president of RAeS.
1953	Received knighthood.
1954	President of RAeS.

CANTRILL, Harry, MIMechE, FRAeS – born 1891

1914-18	Served in the RNAS and RAF.
1919-37	Development and Chief Engineer – Armstrong Siddeley Motors (Aero-engine Division).
1938	Chief Engineer, Rolls-Royce Aero Division.

COX, Sir Harold Roxbee, DSc, PhD, DIC, BSc, MIMechE, FRAeS, FIAeS (USA) – Later Lord Kings Norton – 1902-1998

1918-22	Austin Motor Co.
1922-24	Imperial College of Science and Technology.
1924-29	Engineer at the Royal Airship Works.
1929-30	Airworthiness Dept – RAE, Farnborough.
1931-36	Chief technical officer – Royal Airship Works.
1936-38	Head of Air Defence Dept.
1939-40	Superintendent of Scientific Research – RAE.
1940-43	Deputy Director of Scientific Research – Ministry of Aircraft Production.
1944-46	Chairman and Managing Director of Power Jets (Research and Development) Ltd.
1945	Chairman of the Gas Turbine Technical Advisory and Co-ordinating Committee.
1946-48	Director of National Gas Turbine Establishment.
1948-54	Chief Scientist – Ministry of Fuel & Power.
1947-49	President RAeS.

FEDDEN, Sir Alfred Hubert Roy, Kt 1942, MBE, FRSA, DSc, FRAeS, MIME, MSAE, MIAE, Hon FIAS – 1885-1973

1906-08	Draughtsman – Brazil Straker.
1909-14	Works Manager and Chief Engineer – Brazil Straker.
1914-18	Technical Director and Chief Engineer – Brazil Straker (purchase by Cosmos).
1920-42	Technical Director and Chief Engineer – Cosmos (purchased by Bristol Aeroplane Co).
1938-45	President of the RAeS.
1942-45	Special technical adviser to Ministry of Aircraft Production.

1949-50   Member of Council of the RAeS.

DE HAVILLAND, Capt Sir Geoffrey Kt, OM, CBE, AFC, Hon FRAeS, FIAeS (USA) Vice President Royal Aero Club – 1882-1965

1908-9   Designed and built his first aero-engine.
1909   Designed and built his first aeroplane.
1914   (May) – Joined the Aircraft Manufacturing Co Ltd (Airco) as designer.
1914   (Aug) – As RFC reservist was called up and joined No 2 Squadron at Farnborough. Seconded to Airco to resume designing.
1914-19   Extensive designs of various aircraft for the RFC, remained a commissioned officer under secondment.
1920   Formed the de Havilland Aircraft Co Ltd.
1920-55   Managing Director of de Havilland Aircraft Co Ltd.
1943   Vice-president RAeS.
1944   Received knighthood.
1950   Awarded the RAeS Gold Medal.
1955   Chairman of DH Holdings Ltd.

DE HAVILLAND, Major Hereward DSO – born 1894

1913-14   Test pilot at the Royal Aircraft Factory, Farnborough.
1914-18   Serviced in the RFC and RAF.
1919-24   Represented de Havilland Aircraft Co in Madrid.
1927-34   Managing Director – de Havilland Aircraft (Pty) Ltd, Australia.
1934-39   Area manager – de Havilland Aircraft Co in Central and South America.

HAWKER, Harry George, MBE, AFC 1889-1921

1911   Came to England in May from Australia as a skilled mechanic.
1912   Joined Sopwith at Brooklands as mechanic under F Sigrist, the works manager.
          Learnt to fly and obtained Royal Aero Club Cert No 297.
          Successful at flying competitions at Brooklands.
1913   Achieved British height record with a Sopwith tractor biplane at 11,450 feet.

1914	(Jan) – Returned to Australia to demonstrate Sopwith Tabloid. (May) – Returned to Brooklands and, on the 18th, was the first to attempt to fly the Atlantic, with Lt Cdr Mackenzie Grieve as navigator, starting from St John's, Newfoundland. The attempt failed; was rescued from sea. Awarded the Air Force Cross for his effort.
1914-18	Continued to design and test Sopwith aircraft needed by the RFC.
1920-21	Raced at Brooklands with Mercedes, Austro-Daimler and Sunbeam cars. Sopwith Company wound up in November 1920, Hawker formed H G Hawker Engineering Co with Sigrist and Eyre joining him as Directors. Sopwith joined later.
1921	Killed on 6 July whilst piloting a Nieuport Goshawk at an aerial display at Hendon.

HENDERSON, Lt Gen Sir David 1862-1921

1912	As Brigadier, was Director of Military Training at the War Office, responsible for establishing the RFC in May 1912. He was one of the eleven army pilots at that time.
1915-16	Responsible for the RFC as Lt Gen. Appointed a permanent seat on the Army Council and became member of the newly-formed Joint War Air Committee.
1917	Transferred to the Air Ministry.
1918	Vice-president of the Air Council.

HIVES, Ernest Walter, 1st Baron of Duffield, CH, MBE, LID, DSc, FRAeS – 1886-1965

1908	Joined Rolls-Royce Ltd.
1914	Head of car Experimental Dept and chief test driver.
1936	Appointed to the Board.
1946	Director and General Manager of Rolls-Royce and director of Rotol Airscrews Ltd.
1948	Managing Director of Rolls-Royce.
1950	Raised to the peerage.
1955	Executive Chairman of Rolls-Royce.
1956	Retired from Rolls-Royce.

HOOKER, Sir Stanley G, OBE, ARCSc, BSc, DIC, DPhil, FRAeS, FRSA –
1907-1984

1935	Scientific Officer at Admiralty Laboratories, Teddington seconded to ballistic research at Woolwich Arsenal.
1938	Joined Rolls-Royce – in charge of supercharger development for aero-engines.
1940	Chief assistant to chief experimental engineer.
1942	Assisted Frank Whittle with centrifugal compressor data and, in November, was appointed chief engineer of Rolls-Royce jet engine development.
1948	(Dec) – Resigned from Rolls-Royce and, in January 1949, joined the Engine Division of Bristol Aeroplane Co. In mid 1950, became Chief Engineer of Engine Division.
1963	Technical Director of Bristol Siddeley Engines Ltd.
1967	Retired from BSEL but continued as consultant.
1970	Returned to Rolls-Royce as Technical Director specifically to sort out problems on the RB211 engine.
1971	Following collapse of Rolls-Royce, was appointed Technical Director of Government-owned Rolls-Royce (1971) Ltd.
1974	Received knighthood.
1978	Retired.

KENILWORTH, Lord J D, 1st Baron (J D Siddeley) Kt, CBE, FRAeS, Hon
MIMechE, Past President of Society of British Aircraft Constructors – born
1866

Refer to Armstrong Siddeley Motors entry under Companies section.

MOULT, Dr Ernest Stanley PhD, BSc (Eng), MIMechE, FRAeS – born 1903

1921	Engineering student with Peter Hooker Ltd.
1924	Newall Engineering Co.
1927	Joined Halford as technical assistant.
1944	Appointed Chief Engineer of Engine & Propeller Division of de Havilland Aircraft Co Ltd.
1951-54	Member of Council of the RAeS.
1955	Director of de Havilland Engine Co Ltd.
1957	Technical Director of the Engine Co.

RICARDO, Sir Harry Ralph, LLD, Hon FRS, BA, Hon MIME, MASME, FRAeS 1885-1974

> Founder, Chairman and Technical Director of Messrs Ricardo & Co Engineers (1927) Ltd.
>
> For details of career – refer to section on Companies.

ROE, Sir Alliott Vernon, OBE, FRAeS, FIAeS – 1877-1958

1902	Completed apprenticeship with Lancashire & Yorkshire Railway locoworks.
1903-5	Draughtsman in the motor industry.
1907	Learnt to fly and received aviators certificate No 18.
1908	Designed and built his first aircraft and achieved first (unofficial) flight in England.
1910	Formed A V Roe & Co Ltd with his brother.
1928	Sold A V Roe & Co and acquired an interest in S E Saunders Ltd, Cowes, builders of flying boats, Company then became Saunders-Roe Ltd.

SIGRIST, Frederick, MBE, FRAeS – 1880-1956

1910	Aircraft designer with T O M Sopwith.
1914-18	Founder member of the Hawker Aircraft Co Ltd.
1927	Managing Director of the Gloster Aircraft Co Ltd.
1935	Director of the Sopwith Aeroplane Co Ltd, Armstrong Siddeley, A V Roe, Air Service Training and Armstrong Whitworth Aviation.

SOPWITH, Sir Thomas Octave Murdock, CBE, FRAeS 1888-1989

1910	Learnt to fly and received aviators certificate No 31.
1913	Founded the Sopwith Aviation Co Ltd and designed and constructed all Sopwith aircraft.
1914-18	Designed and produced a variety of aircraft for the RFC and RNAS.
1925-27	Joint Managing Director Hawker Aircraft Co Ltd.

1935	Formed a Trust Company to acquire the shares of Armstrong Siddeley Development Co and also a holding company named Hawker Siddeley Aircraft Co Ltd. Within this holding company was Armstrong Siddeley Motors, Armstrong Whitworth Aircraft, A V Roe (AVRO) and Air Service Training. Held office as chairman.

TIZARD, Sir Henry Thomas, GCB, AFC, FRS, FRAeS, FIAeS, FInstP, Member of the National Research & Development Corporation – born 1885

1911-21	Fellow of Oriel College, Oxford, Lecturer in natural science.
1914	Enlisted in the Army. In 1915, transferred to the RFC.
1918-19	Assistant Controller, Experiments and Research – RAE.
1927-29	Permanent Secretary – Dept of Scientific & Industrial Research.
1933-43	Chairman of the Aeronautical Research Committee.
1941-43	Member of Council of Ministry of Aircraft Production and Member of the Air Council.
1946-52	Chairman of Defence Research Policy Committee, Ministry of Defence.
1948	President of the British Association.

WHITTLE, Air Commodore Sir Frank, KBE, CB, MAScD, DScLiD, FRS, MIMechE, FRAeS 1907-1996

1923-26	Apprentice at RAF Cranwell.
1926-28	Cadetship on passing out at Cranwell.
1931-32	Test pilot – Marine Aircraft Experimental Establishment.
1932-34	Engineering course – RAF Henlow.
1934-37	Cambridge University – science tripos.
1937-45	Research on jet propulsion gas turbines.
1946-48	Technical adviser on engine design and production to Controller of Supplies (Air) Ministry of Supply.
1948	Retired from RAF with rank of Air Commodore.
1948	Awarded KBE.
1954	With Dutch Royal Shell Group.

KERR WILSON, Dr William DSc (Eng), PhD, MSc, WhEx, MIMechE, MNEC, Inst Member of Council of Mech Eng 1944 – born 1897

1915-19	Apprentice in marine engineering at William Doxford & Sons Ltd, Sunderland

1919-35	Assistant Chief Designer – Oil Engine Dept, Doxford
1936-40	Resident technical consultant, Engine & Propeller Divisions – de Havilland Aircraft Co Ltd
1940-60	Chief Research Engineer – de Havilland Engine Co Ltd. Published The Balancing of Oil Engines and Practical Solutions of Torsional Vibration Problems. Both these publications became standard references.

Companies

The following section details those companies with whom Halford had involvement, beginning in 1916 when a technical member of the Royal Flying Corps, throughout his career.

AIRCRAFT DISPOSAL COMPANY (AIRDISCO)

Immediately following the end of World War I, the Ministry of Munitions were faced with the need to dispose of the considerable stocks of aircraft and aircraft engines, either redundant from the needs of the RAF or new stocks delivered too late for service in the war. These stocks were assembled at the National Aircraft Factories at Castle Bromwich, Heaton Chapel, Aintree and Waddon (Croydon). The Aircraft Disposal Board was set up to auction this vast amount of material, but the Board's method produced unfair competition with the aircraft industry and gave no consideration to the safety in the manner to which such items would be used. Parliament reviewed the situation and agreed that only competent aircraft companies, able to regulate the sale in a manner that would ensure safe usage of the items to be disposed, would be allowed to bid.

Handley Page Ltd offered one million pounds and this was accepted conditional to the inclusion of a clause in the agreement giving the Treasury a fifty percent share of the profits. On 18 March 1920, the entire stocks were handed over to the Aircraft Disposal Company, which Handley Page had registered on 4 March with a capital of £600. Airdisco, as the Company became known, then appointed Handley Page Ltd as sole agent. Lucrative sales continued for the next five years. Then, on 30 July 1925, a new company – ADC Aircraft Ltd – took over all the assets of Airdisco. The stock items of interest in this narrative is the 30,000 aero-engines; 3000 of the new engines, redesigned by Halford using many existing parts from the stock, were sold and the Treasury benefited by three times the expected amount under the profit-sharing agreement.

ARMSTRONG SIDDELEY MOTORS LTD – Coventry

In 1909, J D Siddeley was appointed General Manager of the Deasy Motor Car Co and, in 1912, the name was changed to the Siddeley-Deasy Motor Car Co. Early in the First World War, the Company received orders to build the RAF engines. This was followed in 1916 by orders to produce the BHP engine. As the initial design failed its 50-hour test, the Chief Designer – F R Smith – undertook redesign. He was assisted by Major F M Green, who left the Royal Aircraft Factory at Farnborough, bringing with him details of the RAF 8 radial engine and the services of designer, S D Heron. The redesigned BHP emerged as the Puma and a large number were produced, the output rising to 160 per week by the end of the war.

In 1918, the design work on the RAF 8 started. This 14-cylinder two-row radial engine, rated at 360 bhp, was named the Jaguar. In 1924, it was producing 425 bhp and in 1925 a supercharged version was available. A series of radial engines were produced and, by 1933, included the following range: Genet 75-105 bhp, Lynx 200-250 bhp, Mongoose 150 bhp, Cheetah 290-420 bhp, Serval 340 bhp, Jaguar 385-500 bhp, Panther 525-730, Tiger 850 bhp.

J D Siddeley actively backed W C Devereux in forming the successful High Duty Alloys Ltd. In 1925, the company became Armstrong Siddeley Motors Ltd, part of the Armstrong Siddeley Development Co Ltd then, in 1935, it was Hawker Siddeley Co Ltd. A Ministry contract in 1942 to produce a compressor unit from a Farnborough design led the company into the gas turbine field and the Python turbo-prop engine of 3600 bhp plus 1100 lb thrust resulted. They continued with aero gas turbines and produced the Mamba, Adder, Double Mamba and Viper. Hawker Siddeley merged with Bristol Aero-engines to form Bristol Siddeley Engines Ltd in 1959 and, in October 1966, was incorporated into Rolls-Royce.

ARROL-JOHNSTON

The year 1895 saw the creation of the Mo-Car Syndicate Ltd of Bluevale, Camlachie, Glasgow. The directors were George Johnston, a locomotive engineer, Norman Osbourne Fulton, a cousin of Johnston, and Thomas Blackwood Murray. The venture was financed by the architect of the Forth Bridge, Sir William Arrol, and its purpose was to manufacture the Arrol-Johnston motor car.

In 1899, Blackwood Murray and Fulton left to form the Albion Motorcar Company Ltd. 1904 brought the Mo-Car Syndicate into the commercial vehicle market and, in 1905, a Mr J S Napier joined as Chief Engineer, following which a new company, The Arrol-Johnston Car Company Ltd, was formed with the backing of Sir William Beardmore, who became Chairman.

At Arrol-Johnston, production increased and, following a fire in 1906, a move was made to Underwood at Paisley. In 1909, they appointed Mr T C Pullinger as General Manager. He had previously worked with the Sunbeam and Humber motor companies. A further move to Heathhall at Dumfries was carried out in 1913. Starting in 1914, the company was engaged in war work including the manufacture of aero-engines in a new factory at Tongland, Kirkcudbright.

Arrol-Johnson continued car manufacture with mixed success. They were one of the earliest companies to market a new model after the war, the 18-horsepower Victory. This was the design of a newcomer to the company, a Mr G W A Brown, who had been a designer with Clement-Talbot. This was followed by a light car named the Galloway (the design of which was similar to the Fiat 501). In 1924, the Tongland factory was closed and Galloway production transferred to Heathhall. Three years later, Arrol-Johnston amalgamated with Aster, of Wembley, Middlesex, who were an engine manufacturer who had started producing commercial vehicles in 1922. The amalgamated company produced the Arrol-Johnston, the Galloway and the Arrol Aster.

Late in 1927, they rebuilt Sir Malcolm Campbell's Bluebird, an Arrol Aster special with a Napier engine for an attempt on the world land speed record in February 1928 and to be run at Vernouk Pan, South Africa. The company went into liquidation in 1929. The liquidators continued to produce a small number of Arrol Asters until the business finally ended in 1931.

BEARDMORE COMPANIES

In 1861, William Beardmore was a partner in Parkhead Forge, Glasgow. When he died in 1877, his son – also William – carried on the business adding steel production which, by 1890, made the company a specialist in armour plate. A site was acquired at Dalmuir where, in 1900, Beardmore became a major constructor of warships. From 1901 to 1907, William Beardmore held the Chairmanship of J I Thornicroft whose design of steam vehicles were made in Scotland by Duncan Stewart & Co. William Beardmore was a director.

The formation of William Beardmore & Co Ltd took place in 1902 with Maxim Ltd and Vickers & Sons holding 50% of the equity. (Vickers remained involved until it merged with Sir W G Armstrong-Whitworth in 1927). William Beardmore was also the largest shareholder in the Arrol-Johnston Co. The Beardmore Co made car chassis for a number of firms. This gave the company 20% of its revenue.

In March 1914, Beardmore obtained a licence to build the 120 hp Austro-Daimler aero-engine and a new company was registered as the Beardmore Austro-Daimler Aero Engines Ltd. They modified the engine by adding twin carburettors and dual ignition. Manufacture continued through to 1917. The Galloway Engineering Company was one of Beardmore's subsidiary companies. During the First World War, Beardmore companies manufactured ships, airships, aircraft, tanks and armaments.

The design and manufacture of the 840 hp Cyclone was undertaken in 1919 and continued through to 1922 and in 1924 a four-stroke diesel of eight cylinders, the Tornado of 585 hp, was produced for installation in the airship R101.

Post-war the Beardmore Motor Car Co Ltd in Glasgow produced an 11 hp model and continued the Arrol-Johnston range of cars. They bought Alley & MacLellen manufacturing steam locomotives and the Beardmore Precision motor cycle continued in Birmingham, together with the Dunelt motor cycle in Sheffield.

In the late 1920s, car manufacture was concentrated on the production of taxis and some 6000 were supplied to London by 1928. Taxis were made until 1939, then reintroduced in 1954 through to 1967. The company was bought by the Firth-Brown Group in 1957 and, by 1975, the Beardmore name had disappeared. Sir William Beardmore became Lord Invernairn in 1921 and died in 1936.

BLACKBURN AEROPLANE & MOTOR CO LTD – Brough, East Yorks

In 1910, Robert Blackburn started building aircraft and achieved success with a 80 hp monoplane by winning the Inter County 100 miles Air Race.

In 1914, the company was contracted to build the Sopwith Schneider seaplane for the Air Department of the Admiralty. This was developed as the Blackburn Baby seaplane. The Company purchased the Hermes Engine Co Ltd, and with it acquired the range of Cirrus engines, in 1934.

In 1939-45, the company was contracted to repair de Havilland Gipsy engines. Post 1945, the new four-cylinder 180 bhp Bombardier engine was produced. In 1951, a licence was obtained to manufacture the French Turbomeca turbine engine and, in 1958, they produced a modified Turbomeca Artouste turbo jet.

DE HAVILLAND AIRCRAFT CO LTD

Geoffrey de Havilland left Aircraft Manufacturing Co Ltd in 1919 and started his own company. The de Havilland Aircraft Co Ltd was incorporated on 25 September 1920 with an authorised capital of £50,000 and, in October, the company set up their works at Stag Lane, Edgware, Middlesex.

De Havilland set out to design and build a series of light aircraft which would be within the pocket of those who were able to run a luxury car. He was keen to promote interest in flying to a wider public and to stimulate the creation of local flying clubs. To this end, de Havilland School of Flying was formed in April 1923 at the Stag Lane Aerodrome, adjacent to the Company works. The two decades of the 20s and 30s saw many designs of light aircraft produced, both for the private flyer and for the small commercial market. Aided by Halford's reliable and economic engines, sales grew to cover a world-wide market and companies were set up in Australia, Canada, New Zealand, Rhodesia and South Africa. In the years between the wars, de Havilland were one of the largest civil aircraft manufacturers in the world.

The DH Forge Ltd was started in 1941, the DH Engine Co Ltd in 1944 and the DH Propellers Co Ltd in 1946. DH took complete control of Airspeed Ltd in 1948. November 1955 saw the need to reorganise and provide improved control of all the companies. This led to the incorporation of the DH Holdings Ltd as a parent company. The business continued to expand with the Nuclear Power Group created in 1958 and the Industrial Power Group in 1959. The following year was the start of a massive reshaping of the industry in Britain and aircraft producers were merged into conglomerates. DH Propellers became DH Dynamics and combined with Hawker Siddeley guided weapons and rocket division.

By 1961, the Bristol Siddeley Engine Company acquired DH Engine Co and the Blackburn Engine Co from Hawker Siddeley then they, in turn, were absorbed by Rolls-Royce on 5 October 1966.

HERMES ENGINE COMPANY LTD – Croydon

This company undertook the manufacture of the Cirrus range of engines in 1926 from Airdisco when Airdisco ceased trading. Engines were then marketed as Cirrus Hermes. They continued to design and produce further engines in the shape of the Hermes II, III and IV. The Hermes Engine Company was purchased by the Blackburn Aircraft Company in 1934 at which time the Cirrus Minor engine was under initial test.

POWER JETS LIMITED

Power Jets Ltd was incorporated in March 1936 with an authorised capital of £10,000. Directors were L L Whyte of the investment bankers, O T Falk & Partners, and Sir Maurice Bonham Carter, also a director of Falk & Partners who were 'B' shareholders, R Dudley Williams and J C B Tilling the 'A' shareholders. Frank Whittle was a shareholder and acted as honorary chief engineer and technical consultant. He was a serving officer in the RAF and the Service would only allow him six hours per week to devote to Power Jets. BTH were approached and agreed to a contract with Power Jets to produce design drawings for an experimental engine.

In January 1940, Whittle met Maurice Wilks, chief engineer of the Rover Car Company and suggested that Power Jets should place a contract with Rover for the manufacture of an experimental engine. Rover agreed to a contract. Meetings with the Air Ministry in March 1940 resulted in defining the policy of future development and manufacture. The Crown exercised its right to the free use of Power Jets patents and the Air Ministry (which in May of that year became the Ministry of Aircraft Production with Lord Beaverbrook as the Minister) placed direct contracts for the manufacture of the engine with both the Rover Company and BTH, Power Jets being responsible for design and development. The engine to be produced was the W2B designed to give a static thrust of 1800 lb and scheduled for the F9/40 fighter.

In April 1944, the Government nationalised Power Jets Ltd and a new company Power Jets (Research & Development) Ltd was created. Frank Whittle was appointed chief technical adviser to the Board. Although a private company under the Companies Act, all shares were owned by the Government. The purpose of the Company was to ensure the Government owned and managed all the patents related to gas turbines taken out by Power Jets Ltd. The new company also acted as technical consultants and operated the School of Gas Turbine Technology.

Whittle resigned from the Board of Power Jets (R&D) Ltd in January 1946 and, by March of that year, the company became a small patent-holding company losing all experimental and manufacturing rights to the National Gas Turbine Establishment.

RICARDO CONSULTING ENGINEERS LTD – Shoreham by Sea

In 1917 Harry Ricardo registered his company as Engine Patents Ltd with an authorised capital of £20,000. 1919 saw the name changed to Ricardo & Co when the work undertaken under the original name had proved successful. The company received a three-year contract from Shell Oil to investigate the fuels Shell processed from oilfields in various parts of the world. The purpose being to establish those fuels with the better 'anti-knock' content. In 1921, a move was made to the new laboratory/works at Bridge Works, Shoreham by Sea and a research contract was started for the Air Ministry. This was on an annual renewal basis and it continued for the next twenty-five years. This research was to undertake to improve fuel economy of aero-engines, either by the preparation of fuels or by mechanical design.

Investigation into the efficiency of double- or single-sleeve valve engines and of poppet-valve engines, also research into the design of compression-ignition and spark- ignition engines. This led to the development of the famous 'slipper piston' and the 'turbulent cylinder head'. A series of patents were obtained for these particular designs and both these areas have provided a sound basis for the company's success, still being modified and developed to this day. Between the 1920/30s, Ricardo established a reputation for sound progress in improving the combustion efficiency of the internal combustion engine.

The name of the company was again changed, to that it still trades under – Ricardo Consulting Engineers Ltd. From 1940 to 1944, the Company transferred its operations to Oxford for the period of hostilities, following which it returned to its Shoreham base where it still operates. Up to the present day, Ricardo Consulting Engineers Ltd continues to provide a highly sophisticated design service, using the most modern facilities of computer and electronics to serve the design needs of many world-wide engine manufacturers and automobile companies.

APPENDIX II

Government orders for aero-engines
from August 1914 to December 1918
(Compiled from PRO File: Air 1/ 2301/215/12)

TYPE	RATED hp	No ORDERED	No DELIVERED
BRITISH			
ABC Gnat	30	18	17
ABC Wasp	170	268	26
ABC Dragonfly	300	10098	827
Anzani	100	125	125
Beardmore	120	400	400
Beardmore	160	2937	2246
BHP	230	12560	4382
BR1	150	1730	1123
BR2	200	6300	2566
Clerget	80	553	142
Clerget	100/130	1300	1300
Clerget	140	1750	1750
Galloway Atlantic	500	800	73
Gnome	50	20	8
Gnome	80	1542	979
Green	100	42	42
Green	275	75	21
Hispano-Suiza	150/180	4350	2039
Hispano-Suiza	200	26	–
Le Rhone	80	2350	1488
Le Rhone	110/120	2300	1974
Monognome	100	5630	2188
Napier	400	100	35
RAF 1a	90	2960	2850
RAF 1b	100	115	114
RAF 3a	200	290	289
RAF 4a	140/150	3610	3608
RAF 4d	180	500	16
Renault	70/75	427	427
Renault	80	5261	2004
Rolls-Royce Hawk	75/90	300	206
Rolls-Royce Falcon	190/200	2175	1132

TYPE	RATED hp	No ORDERED	No DELIVERED
Rolls-Royce Eagle	250/360	5600	3111
Rolls-Royce Condor	600	100	–
Salmson	135	106	106
Salmson	200	36	36
Sunbeam Viking	50	50	9
Sunbeam Dyak	100	160	–
Sunbeam	110	7	7
Sunbeam Crusader	150	224	224
Sunbeam Nubian	155	50	36
Sunbeam Zulu	160	75	75
Sunbeam Amazon	170	100	77
Sunbeam Afridi	200	300	299
Sunbeam Arab	200	5160	1195
Sunbeam Ghurka	240	83	83
Sunbeam Maori	250/275	1063	974
Sunbeam Mohawk	287	290	287
Sunbeam Manitou	300	840	13
Sunbeam Cossack	316/320	312	312

FRENCH

TYPE	RATED hp	No ORDERED	No DELIVERED
Anzani	90/100	365	365
Anzani	125	59	59
Canton Unné	130/140	68	68
Canton Unné	150/160	245	245
Clerget	80	21	21
Clerget	100	271	271
Clerget	130	1865	1865
Clerget	200	2100	889
Gnome	50	32	32
Gnome	80	143	143
Hispano-Suiza	150	150	150
Hispano-Suiza	180	25	25
Hispano-Suiza	200	5410	5410
Hispano-Suiza	300	4205	329
Le Rhone	60	114	114
Le Rhone	80	1372	1341
Le Rhone	110	1000	-
Le Rhone	120	1629	1553
Mercedes	130	142	142
Monognome	100	356	310

TYPE	RATED hp	No ORDERED	No DELIVERED
Renault	70	196	196
Renault	80	43	43
Renault	110	9	9
Renault	200	452	452
ITALIAN			
Fiat	250/300	1738	610
Fiat	500	6	6
Isotta	160	6	6
AMERICAN			
Curtiss VK		578	168
Curtiss OX5		2041	2041
Liberty	400	3215	2209

	1914	1915	1916	1917	1918
Delivered per year	99	1721	5363	11763	22088

Total number of engines ordered: 87,629

Total number of engines delivered: 41,044

The disparity between numbers ordered and delivered was due to large orders placed in 1917 and 1918 which could not be completed before the Armistice upon which the Government rapidly issued cancellations.

APPENDIX III

Initial Royal Flying Corps Establishment in France – 1914
Squadron Aircraft and Engines

On 13 August 1914, the RFC set up operational bases in France at Amiens and St Omer. Four squadrons, all that could be mustered, were deployed each with a variety of aircraft and engines.

No 2 Squadron   with Royal Aircraft Factory BE2a &2b and RE1 & RE5, Maurice Farman S7 Longhorn and S11 Shorthorn.

No 3 Squadron   with Nieuport Monoplane, Deperdussin Monoplane, Bristol Monoplane and Boxkite, BE2c,3&4, Avro 500, Sopwith Tabloid.

No 4 Squadron   with S11 Shorthorn, S7 Longhorn, Martinsyde Scout, BE2 & 2b

No 5 Squadron   with Voisin Biplane, Caudron G3&4, Avro 504j & 504k, Bristol Bullet D, Vickers FB5, Martinsyde Scout A

In October, No 6 Squadron was deployed to Belgium with 13 aircraft including BE2c& BE2d, FE2a & FE2b, Voisin Biplane.

In December, No 9 Squadron was deployed to St Omer with BE2, Bleriot XI, S7 Longhorn, S11 Shorthorn

In the first half of 1915, two further squadrons were stationed at St Omer:

On 7 March, No 1 Squadron equipped with Avro 504, Bristol Scout D, Caudron G3 & G4

On 8 April, No 7 Squadron with RE5, BE2 & BE8, Morane Biplane, Bleriot XI, Henry Farman F20, Sopwith Tabloid

With this variety of aircraft came an even greater variety of engines. The following engines powered these aircraft:-

60hp Renault	BE2c& BE2d, RE1, Boxkite
70hp Renault	BE2a & BE2b, BE3 & BE4, Caudron G3 & G4, Longhorn, RE1
70hp Gnome	Bleriot XI
80hp Gnome	Avro 500 & 504K, Bristol Scout D, Caudron G3 & G4, Martinsyde Scout A, Morane Saulnier, Henry Farman F20, BE8, Sopwith Tabloid
80hp Le Rhone	Avro 500 & 504K, Bristol Scout D, Caudron G3&4, Morane Saulnier, Henry Farman F20
80hp Clerget	Avro 500 & 504K, BE8
100hp Gnome	Avro 504j & 504k, Deperdussin, Vickers FB5, Sopwith Tabloid, BE8
100hp Anzani	Caudron G3 & G4, Deperdussin
110hp Le Rhone	Avro 504K, Vickers FB5
110hp Clerget	Vickers FB5
120hp Austro Damlier	RE5
130hp Clerget	Avro 504K
130 & 140hp Salmson	Voisin Biplane

APPENDIX IV

Halford Engines

Year	Name	Type (see*)	Capacity Litres	No. Cylinders	bhp at rpm	Bore M/M	Stroke M/M	Coolant
AERO ENGINES								
1915	Beardmore	ILU	18.85	6	120 up to 160 at 1400	145	190	Water
1916	BHP Adriatic	ILU	18.85	6	160 at 1400	145	190	Water
1917	BHP Puma	ILU	18.85	6	230 at 1400	145	190	Water
1918	BHP Atlantic and Pacific	VEE U	37.6	12	500 at 1500	145	190	Water
1918	RHA	VEE INV	14.25	12	300 at 1500			Water
1924	Airdisco	VEE U	9	8	144 at 2000	105	130	Air
1924	Nimbus	ILU	20.7	6	335 at 1600	152	190	Water
1925	Cirrus I	ILU	4.5	4	68 at 2000	105	130	Air
1926	Cirrus II	ILU	4.95	4	80 at 1800	110	130	Air
1926	Cirrus III	ILU	5.23	4	90 at 1800	118	130	Air
1926	CirrusIV	ILU	4.95	4	105 at 2000	110	130	Air
1927	Gipsy R	ILU	5.5	4	135 at 2650	114	128	Air
1927	Gipsy I	ILU	5.23	4	98 at 2100	114	128	Air
1929	Gipsy II	ILU	5.71	4	120 at 2300	114	140	Air
1929	Ghost	VEE U	8.15	8	200 at2000	114	128	Air
1929	Rapier	H super-charged	8.55	16	300 to 400 at 3500	90	90	Air
1930	Gipsy III	IL INV	6.12	4	130 at 2300	118	140	Air
1931	Gipsy IV	IL INV	3.9	4	80 at 2000	102	120	Air
1932	Gipsy Major I	IL INV	6.12	4	130 at 2300	118	140	Air
1932	Javellin	IL INV	8.2	6	135 at 2100	115	133	Air
1933	Gipsy Six I	IL INV	9.18	6	200 at2350	118	140	Air
1934	Dagger	H Super-charged	16.8	24	610 to 925 at 4000	97	95	Air
1934	Gipsy Six R	IL INV	9.18	6	230 at 2350	118	140	Air
1934	Gipsy Six II	IL INV geared	9.18	6	225 at 2900	118	140	Air
1935	Gipsy Twelve	VEE INV	18.37	12	525 at 2600	118	140	Air
1935	Gipsy Major II	IL INV	6.12	4	138 at 2500	118	140	Air
1935	Gipsy Queen I	IL INV	9.18	6	205 at 2400	118	140	Air
1935	Gipsy Queen II	IL INV	9.18	6	210 at 2700	118	140	Air

164

Manufacturers	Production	Installed in Aircraft	Note
Beardmore & Galloway Eng Co		DH 1 and 4	Austro Daimler under licence
Galloway Engine Co and	6000	DH 4	Beardmore Halford Pullenger
Siddeley Deasy Motor Co			
Siddeley Deasy Motor Co		DH 4, 9, 50, 50A	
Siddeley Deasy Motor Co		DH 9	
Siddeley Deasy Motor Co	3	DH 4	Ricardo Halford Armstrong
Aircraft Disposal Co		DH 51	
Aircraft Disposal Co	700	DH 9	Uprated Puma
Aircraft Disposal Co	700	DH 60 Moth	
Aircraft Disposal Co	650	DH 60 Moth	
Hermes Engineering Co	250		
Hermes Engineering Co			
de Havilland Aircraft Co	2	DH 71 Gipsy Moth	Racing monoplane
de Havilland Aircraft Co	1450	DH 60 Gipsy Moth, Metal Gipsy Moth, DH 71 Tiger Moth	
de Havilland Aircraft Co	310	DH 60 and Puss Moth	
de Havilland Aircraft Co		DH 75 Hawk Moth	
D Naiper & Son	120	DH 77 Fairey Sea Fox/ Mercury	Mercury was upper component of Mayo composite
de Havilland Aircraft Co	611	DH 80A Puss Moth	
de Havilland Aircraft Co	4	DH 18 Swallow Moth	
de Havilland Aircraft Co	14615	DH 60, 80A, 83 Fox Moth	2 No. Major - DH 84 Dragon - DH 90 Dragonfly
D Napier & Son	50	Percival Gull and Gull IV Percival P2 Mew Gull	Spartan Arrow Martin Baker MBI
de Havilland Aircraft Co	1140	DH 86 and 89	
D Napier & Son	590	Hawker Hector Handley Page Hereford	
de Havilland Aircraft Co	8	DH 88 Comet	London/Australia
de Havilland Aircraft Co	248	2 No. Six II - DH 88, DH 86A	
de Havilland Aircraft Co	90	DH 91 Albatross DH 93 Don	Service version - Gipsy King Supercharged and geared
de Havilland Aircraft Co	91		
de Havilland Aircraft Co			Initially engines were Ministry versions
de Havilland Aircraft Co	1780		

Year	Name	Type (see*)	Capacity Litres	No. Cylinders	bhp at rpm	Bore M/M	Stroke M/M	Coolant
AERO ENGINES								
1937	Gipsy Minor	IL INV	3.76	4	90 at 2250	102	115	Air
1937	Sabre	H	36.7	24	3-4000 at 3700	127	120	Water
1939	Gipsy Queen II	IL INV	9.18	6	200 at 2700	118	140	Air
1941	Goblin 1 and 2	Gas turbine	-	-	2700 to 3000lb thrust	-	-	Air
1943	Gipsy Major 30	IL INV	6.12	4	160 at 2500	120	150	Air
1944	Gipsy Major 50	IL INV Super-charged	6.12	4	197 at 2500	120	150	Air
1944	Gipsy Major 10	IL INV	6.12	4	140 at 2500	118	140	Air
1945	Gipsy Queen 31	IL INV	10.18	6	250 at 2500	120	150	Air
1945	Gipsy Queen 51	IL INV super-charged	10.18	6	295 at 2500	120	150	Air
1945	Gipsy Queen 71	IL INV super-charged and geared	10.18	6	330 at 2800	120	150	Air
1945	Ghost I	Gas turbine	-	-	4400lb thrust	-	-	Air
1945	Ghost 103 Mk 1	Gas turbine	-	-	4850lb thrust	-	-	Air
1946	Ghost 50	Gas turbine	-	-	5050lb thrust	-	-	Air
1945	H3 turboshaft prototype	Gas turbine	-	-	500bhp	-	-	Air
1948	Gipsy Major 8, 10 Mk 2	IL INV	6.12	4	145 at 2550	118	140	Air
1948	Goblin 3	Gas turbine	-	-	3500lb thrust	-	-	Air
1949	Sprite	Rocket engine	-	-	5000lb thrust	-	-	-
1950	Gipsy Major 200	IL INV	6.79	4	200 at 2500	120	150	Air
1951	Ghost 104	Gas turbine	-	-	4850lb thrust	-	-	Air
1951	Spectre I Rocket	Variable thrust	-	-	7000lb max thrust	-	-	Air
1953	Gyron junior	DGJI turbojet	-	-	7000lb thrust	-	-	Air
1954	Spectre 4, 5	Rocket engine	-	-	8000lb thrust	-	-	Air
1954	Super Sprite	Rocket engine	-	-	4000lb thrust	-	-	-
1954	Ghost 105	Gas turbine	-	-	5300lb thrust	-	-	-
1955	Gyron Junior	DGJ 10 turbojet	-	-	14000lb reheat	-	-	-
1956	Gipsy Major 215	IL INV super-charged	6.79	4	215 at 2500	120	150	Air
RACING CAR ENGINE								
1923	Halford Special	IL Twin Cam	1500cc	6	Mk 1 96 at 5000 Mk 2 120 at 5500	63	83	Water

Manufacturers	Production	Installed in Aircraft	Note
de Havilland Aircraft Co	170	DH 94	Moth Minor
D Napier & Son	6200	Hawker Typhoon, Tempest	4-port single sleeve valve
de Havilland Aircraft Co	1360	Dominie	
de Havilland Aircraft Co	No. 1-50	Gloster Meteor, Vampire	
	No.2-3600	DH100, DH108	
de Havilland Aircraft Co		Lockheed P80	
de Havilland Aircraft Co			
de Havilland Aircraft Co	590	Miles and Auster	
de Havilland Aircraft Co	1760	DH 114 Heron	
de Havilland Aircraft Co		Percival 'Mersanser'	
de Havilland Aircraft Co	1890	DH 104 Dove and Handley Page 'Marathon'	
de Havilland Aircraft Co	2035	DH 106 Comet	
de Havilland Aircraft Co	1320	DH 112 Venom	
de Havilland Aircraft Co	185	DH 106 Comet	
de Havilland Aircraft Co	Test unit only	Designed for DH Dove development	
de Havilland Aircraft Co	8-950 10-670	Chipmonk	
de Havilland Aircraft Co	2688	DH 115 Vampire Trainer	
de Havilland Aircraft Co	12	DH 106 Comet	
de Havilland Aircraft Co	9	Saro Seeker 10 Helicopter	
de Havilland Aircraft Co	477	DH 106 Comet, DH 112 Venom	
de Havilland Aircraft Co	65		
de Havilland Aircraft Co	112	Blackburn NA 39 'Buccaneer'	
de Havilland Aircraft Co	Spectres 1, 4, 5, 65	ATO for Victor and Saunders Roe, SP 177	
de Havilland Aircraft Co	170	ATO for Valiant	
de Havilland Aircraft Co	53	DH 112 Sea Venom	
de Havilland Aircraft Co	12	Bristol T 188 Supersonic research	
de Havilland Aircraft Co	106	Saro Skeeter 12 Helicopter	
	2	Mk 1 Turbo-supercharger Mk 2 Roots Type super-charger	Redesigned 1925 for use in lifeboats

Year	Name	Type (see*)	Capacity Litres	No. Cylinders	bhp at rpm	Bore M/M	Stroke M/M	Coolant
MOTORCYCLES								
1921	Triumph Ricardo	4 OHV	500cc	1	25 at 5000	80.5	98	Air
1922	Vauxhall	4 OHV	950cc	4	30 at 3000	67	67	Air
OTHER								
1947	Goblin	Gas turbine	-	-	-	-	-	Air
1952	Ghost	Gas turbine	-	-	-	-	-	Air

* ILU - In-line upright
 IL INV - In-line inverted
 H - 4 banks in H configuration

Manufacturers	Production	Installed in Aircraft	Note
Triumph Cycle Co and Ricardo	1	Redesigned by Halford and raced	
Vauxhall	2		
de Havilland Engine Co	1	Adapted for Malcolm Campbell 'Bluebird'	Water speed record attempt
de Havilland Engine Co	1	Adapted for John Cobb 'Crusader'	Water speed record attempt

APPENDIX V

Gipsy engine competition successes

1928	King's Cup Air Race	1st, 3rd, 4th, 5th, 6th, 7th, 11th and 12th. First public appearance of Gipsy engine
	Shoreham Flying Meeting	Winner Climb competition
1929	Air Pageant, New Zealand	Every event – Gipsy Moths 1st and 2nd
	First Mexican Air Race	Gipsy Moths 1st and 2nd
	National Air Race, USA	3rd in 1500 race, Miami to Cleveland 4th – California-Cleveland Derby Four 1sts, one 2nd, two 3rds and two 4ths – Cleveland Closed Circuit 2nd in Cleveland-Toronto
	Canadian National Exhibition Races	1st, 2nd, 3rd and 4th in Toronto-Cleveland 1st, 2nd, 3rd and 4th in St Catherines-Toronto
	Essex Aerial Derby at Windsor, Canada	1st and 2nd
	Australia East to West Race	Fastest time and 2nd, 3rd, 4th, 5th and 6th
	Newcastle Aero Club Meeting	Air League Challenge Cup – 2nd
	International Aerobatic Contest, Heston	1st
	First Inter-City race, Manchester to Liverpool	1st
	Northampton Aero Club	Whitsun Meeting – Silver Cup
	Bristol & Wessex Aero Club	Dessprez Challenge Cup
	Rotterdam International Flying Meeting	1st in speed contest
	Italian Royal Aero Club	Winner in two races
	King's Cup Air Race	Fastest time and 2nd, 3rd, 4th and 5th

	Zenith Cup Air Race – France	Winner
	Britannia Challenge Trophy	Winner
	Challenge International de Tourisme	Category one: 1st, Entire competition: 2nd
1930	Rotterdam International Flying Meeting	Winner in three events plus International Relay Race
	National Flying Pageant, Reading	1st three places in Speed Championship
	Mansfield Robinson Trophy	Winner
	King's Cup Air Race	Fastest time and 2nd and 3rd
	Zenith Cup Air Race – France	Winner and 2nd
	Challenge International de Tourisme	First place and fastest time
1931	Giro Aereo d'Italia	1st, 2nd, 3rd (7 of the first light aircraft were Gipsy-engined)
	Mansfield Robinson Trophy	Winner
	King's Cup Air Race	Three fastest times
	Zenith Cup Air Race	Winner
	Siddeley Trophy	Winner at 128.89mph
	Britannia Challenge Trophy	Winner
	Seagrave Trophy	Winner
	Johnston Memorial Air Navigation Trophy	Winner
	Royal Aero Club Gold Medal	Winner
1932	Hillman Trophy Air Race	Winner
	Mansfield Robinson Trophy	Winner
	Morning Post Trophy	1st, 2nd and 3rd
	McKee Trophy, Canada	Winner
	Inter-City Air Race, Liverpool-Manchester	Winner
	Grosvenor Cup Race	2nd and 3rd
	International Flying Meeting, Warsaw	One 1st, One 2nd
	Austrian Rundflung	Tied for first place
	SBAC Trophy, Portsmouth	1st, 2nd and 3rd
	Portsmouth Challenge Cup	2nd and 3rd

	Weekend Aerien	Winner
	Boulogne Rally	Winner
	International Air Rally at Clermont Ferrand	Winner
	Rally at Boulogne-sur-mer	1st and 2nd
	International Meeting at Zurich	Winner
	King's Cup Air Race	Winner and first nine places
	Zenith Cup Air Race	Winner
	Viceroy's Cup	Winner and second
	Siddeley Trophy	Winner at 129mph
	Seagrave Trophy	Winner
	Johnston Memorial Air Navigation Trophy	Winner
	London-Cardiff Race	Winner
	London-Newcastle Race (Newcastle-upon-Tyne Trophy)	1st and 2nd
	Folkestone Aero Trophy	Winner
1933	Morning Post Trophy	1st and 3rd
	Circuit of Oases, Egypt	Winner of Oases Trophy & Touring Contest
	Peters Challenge Trophy	Winner
	Giro di Lombardia	Won by Gipsy II Breda
	King's Cup Air Race	Winner and 3rd, 6th and 8th
	Zenith Cup Air Race – France	Winner
	Viceroy's Cup	Winner and 2nd
	Britannia Challenge Trophy	Winner
	Seagrave Trophy	Winner
	Johnston Memorial Air Navigation Trophy	Winner
	London-Cardiff Race	Winner
	London-Newcastle Race (Newcastle-upon-Tyne Trophy)	1st and 2nd
	Folkestone Aero Trophy	Winner
1934	MacRobertson International Race, England to Australia	Speed Race – 1st, 4th and 5th Handicap Race – 1st, 3rd and 6th (Relinquished win in favour of Speed prize)
	Palm Trees Circuit	Winner

	Class C Women's Altitude Record	Broken – 4990 metres
	King's Cup Air Race	2nd, 3rd, 5th, 6th, 8th, 9th and 10th
	Viceroy's Cup	Winner
	Siddeley Trophy	Winner at 124.18mph
	Britannia Challenge Trophy	Winner
	Seagrave Trophy	Winner
	London-Newcastle Race (Newcastle-upon-Tyne Trophy)	1st and 2nd
	Royal Aero Club Gold Medal	Winner
	Folkestone Aero Trophy	Winner
1935	Gadammes Rally, North Africa	Winner
	Raduno del Littoria, Italy	Won by Gipsy III-engined Breda
	King's Cup Air Race	First 16 places also 18th, 19th and 20th
	Viceroy's Cup	Winner
	Siddeley Trophy	Winner at 170.08mph
	Britannia Challenge Trophy	Winner
	Johnston Memorial Air Navigation Trophy	Winner
	London-Cardiff Race	Winner
	London-Newcastle Race (Newcastle-upon-Tyne Trophy)	1st and 2nd
	Folkestone Aero Trophy	Winner
1936	Portsmouth to Johannesburg Race	Winner
	London to Isle of Man Air Race	Winner
	King's Cup Air Race	First 26 places – every competitor Gipsy-powered
	Viceroy's Cup	Winner
	Britannia Challenge Trophy	Winner
	Johnston Memorial Air Navigation Trophy	Winner
	London-Cardiff Race	1st, 2nd and 3rd
	London-Newcastle Race (Newcastle-upon-Tyne Trophy)	1st and 2nd
	Royal Aero Club Gold Medal	Winner
	Folkestone Aero Trophy	Winner

1937	Istres – Damascus – Paris Race	4th
	King's Cup Air Race	All 13 places
	Johnston Memorial Air Navigation Trophy	Winner
	London-Cardiff Race	1st, 2nd and 3rd
	London-Newcastle Race (Newcastle-upon-Tyne Trophy)	1st and 2nd
	Royal Aero Club Gold Medal	Winner
	Folkestone Aero Trophy	2nd

Gipsy engine successes, 1927 to 1938

Event	Distance	Time	Crew	Aircraft
1927				
World Speed Record	–	187 mph	Capt Broad	Tiger Moth - Gipsy I prototype
1928				
Gipsy I under seal completed 600 flying hours				

Long Distance and Record Flights

1929				
London-Durban	8000m	39 days	S/L L H Slatter	Bluebird - Gipsy I
London-Nairobi	6000m	78h flying time	F/L F A Swoffer	Gipsy I Moth
UK-India	5500m	3½ months	S/L Drew and Mrs Cleaver	Gipsy I Moth
UK-Australia	10000m	42 days	F C Chichester	Gipsy I Moth
Kenya-UK			Led by Hon F E Guest	3 Gipsy I Moths
Sydney-Adelaide	729m	11h flying time	Capt Grosvenor	Gipsy I Moth
Bonaventure-Bogata	Mails carried by Sociedad Columbo de Alemane de Transportes Aeros			Gipsy I Moth
London-Baghdad		31 days	Salim Sasson Daniel	Gipsy I Moth
Heston-St Ingervert		In Gale	A S Butler and N Norman	2 Gipsy I Moths

1930

Route	Distance	Time	Pilot	Aircraft
London-Port Darwin	10000m	19½ days	Miss A Johnson	Gipsy I Moth
UK-India	5500m	17 days	S P Engineer	Gipsy I Moth
UK-Australia	10000m	10½ days	S/L Kingsford-Smith	Avian - Gipsy II
London-Cape Town	8000m	8½ days 78h flying time	Lt R F Caspereuthus	Puss Moth
England-Malta (Non-stop)	1400m	13h	Capt C D Barnard	Puss Moth - Gipsy III
England-Tangier (Non-stop)	1246m	10½h	Capt C D Barnard	Puss Moth - Gipsy III
Malta-England (Non-stop)	1400m	14½h	Capt C D Barnard	Puss Moth - Gipsy III
Tangier-England (Non-stop)	1240m	10h 55m	M Mohun Singh	Gipsy I Moth
India-UK	5500m	18 days	R N Chawla and S P Engineer	Gipsy I Moth
London-Stockholm (Non-stop)	1040m	12h	Col Master of Semphill	Puss Moth - Gipsy III
Norway-Scotland	300m	3h	Col Master of Semphill	Puss Moth - Gipsy III
UK-Tokyo (Round the world)	30000m	147h flying time	Mrs Victor Bruce	Blackburn Bluebird - Gipsy III
UK-Australia	10000m	33 days	F R Matthews	Puss Moth - Gipsy III
London-Sydney	12000m	20 days	O Garden	Gipsy I Moth
UK-Australia	10000m	37 days	F/L C W Hill	Gipsy III Moth
Abyssinia-Croydon	5000m	5 days	Capt W L Hope	Gipsy III Moth

1931

Route	Distance	Time	Pilot	Aircraft
London-Port Darwin	10000m	9d 3h 40m	C W A Scott	Gipsy II Moth

175

Port Darwin-London	10000m	10d 13h	C W A Scott	Gipsy II Moth
Australia-UK	10000m	8d 22h 35m	J A Mollison	Gipsy II Moth
Lympne-Cape Town	8000m	5d 6h 40m	A G Store and Miss P Salaman	Puss Moth - Gipsy III
Karachi-Lympne	5000m	4½ days	P/O J Grierson	Gipsy I Moth
Paranga Harbour, NZ - Norfolk Island	508m	5h 50m	F C Chichester	Gipsy II Moth
Norfolk Island - Lord Howe Island	575m	7h 40m	F C Chichester	Gipsy II Moth
Australia-NZ	1200m	12h 15m	G Menzies	Avian - Gipsy II
Kenya-UK	8500m	80h 40m	Mrs Wilson and S Mostert	Puss Moth - Gipsy III
UK-Japan	7000m	10 days	Miss A Johnson and C S Humphreys	Puss Moth - Gipsy III
Round Australia	8000m	7d 8h 15m	H F Broadbent	Avian - Gipsy II
New York-Jamaica (Non-stop)	1800m	18h 15m	S/L H J L Hinkler	Puss Moth - Gipsy II
Kingston-Maracaibo	600m	6h	S/L H J L Hinkler	Puss Moth - Gipsy II
Maracaibo-Trinidad-Fortaleza-Nata	2500m	15 days	S/L H J L Hinkler	Puss Moth - Gipsy III
Natal-Bathurst (Non-stop)	2000m	22h	S/L H J L Hinkler	Puss Moth - Gipsy II
Bathurst-Spain-London	3600m	11 days	S/L H J L Hinkler	Puss Moth - Gipsy II
UK-South Africa and return	16000m	72 days (9d 19h flying time)	Capt McIntosh and Mrs R Westenra	Puss Moth - Gipsy III
London-Algiers (Non-stop)	1080m	11h 40m	F/L E H Fielden	Puss Moth - Gipsy III

New Caledonia-Marlborough, Queensland	850m	11h 30m	V Roffey	Gipsy Moth

1932

Lympne-Port Darwin	10000m	8d 20h 47m	C W A Scott	Gipsy II Moth
Lympne-Cape Town	8000m	4d 17h 30m	J A Mollison	Puss Moth - Gipsy III
Lympne-Cape Town	8000m	4d 6h 54m	Mrs A Mollison	Puss Moth - Gipsy Major
Cape Town-Lympne	8000m	7d 7h 5m	Mrs A Mollison	Puss Moth - Gipsy Major
Dublin-New Brunswick (non-stop)	2600m	30h 15m	J A Mollison	Puss Moth - Gipsy III
France-Caledonia (round Australia)	8000m		Mrs H B Bonney	Gipsy I Moth
Cape Town-UK		11 days	Victor Smith	Gipsy II Moth
Lympne-Wyndham, Australia	10000m	7d 4h 44m	Air Comm Sir Kingsford Smith	Percival Gull - Gipsy Major
Lympne-Port Natal, Brazil	4600m	3d 10h 8m	J A Mollison	Puss Moth - Gipsy Major
Pendine-Bridgeport, USA	3300m	39 hrs	Mr & Mrs Mollison	D H Dragon - Gipsy Majors
Warsaw-Brazil			Capt Skarzynski	RWD5 - Gipsy Major

1934

UK-Australia	10000m	14d 23h 25m	Miss J Batten	Metal Moth - Gipsy I
Mildenhall-Melbourne	11300m	60h 50m (flying time)	C W A Scott and T Campbell Black	Comet - Gipsy VI R

Route	Distance	Time	Pilot(s)	Aircraft
Mildenhall-Singapore		39h 56m	C W A Scott and T Campbell Black	Comet - Gipsy VI R
Mildenhall-Darwin	9124m	52h 30m	C W A Scott and T Campbell Black	Comet - Gipsy VI R
Mildenhall-Melbourne Return	23000m	4d 22h 27m (out) 6d 16h 10m (return)	Cathcart Jones and K F H Walker	Comet - Gipsy VI R
Port Darwin-Croydon	10000m	8d 9h	C J Malrose	Moth - Gipsy Major
Mildenhall-Karachi	4500m	23h 13m	Mr & Mrs Mollison	Comet - Gipsy VI R
Mildenhall-Baghdad (Non-stop)	2530m	12h 30m	Mr & Mrs Mollison	Comet - Gipsy VI R
UK-Australia Return	20000m	23d 12h 15d (out) 8d 12h (return)	R Rubin and K F H Walker	Leopard Moth - Gipsy Major
Round Australia	8000m	5d 11h	C J Melrose	Puss Moth - Gipsy Major
Rochester-Ottawa via Greenland	4400m	41h 61m	J Grieson	Fox Moth - Gipsy Major
Ontario-Heston	3500m	30h 50m	L Reid and J R Ayling	Dragon - Gipsy Majors
Brussels-Leopoldville	4441m	22h 46m	K F H Walker and Capt Franchome	Comet - Gipsy VI R
Leopoldville-Brussels	4441m	21h 54m	K F H Walker and Capt Franchome	Comet - Gipsy VI R
Antwerp-Leopoldville-Antwerp		5d - out 8d - return	M & Mde Guy Hausez	Dragon - Gipsy Major
Algiers-Lake Chad via Sahara & Atlas Mts			M G Decamps	Dragon - Gipsy Major

Lisbon-Pangim Nova Goa (India)	6600m	14 days	Senhor Carlos Bleck	Moth - Gipsy Major
Channel flown inverted		25th anniversary of Bleriot's first crossing	F/L G Tyson	Tiger Moth
Agen-Jerusalem-Agen	11890m	5 weeks	M Andre Garric	Puss Moth - Gipsy Major
London-Copenhagen	1400m	at 138.8 mph	Capt T N Stack	Miles Hawk - Gipsy Major
London-Prague		5 hrs	Capt T N Stack	Miles Hawk - Gipsy Major
London-Naples Return	1300m 1300m	at 147.2 mph at 144.4 mph	Capt T N Stack	Miles Hawk - Gipsy Major
1935 Croydon-Port Darwin	9000m	6d 21h 19m	H L Brook	Percival Gull - Gipsy VI
Darwin - Lympne	9000m	7d 19h 50m	Miss J Batten	Miles Falcon - Gipsy Major
Darwin-Croydon	9000m	17d 16h 15m (first women's solo)	Miss J Batten	Metal Moth - Gipsy I
Cape Town-Hanworth	8000m	6d 8h 27m	F/L Llewellyn and Mrs Wyndham	Hendy Heck - Gipsy VI
Hatfield-Cairo	2240m	11h 18m	T Campbell Black	Comet - Gipsy VI R
Gravesend-Oran (non-stop)	2300m	7h 10m out 7h 20m return	Capt E W Percival	Percival Gull - Gipsy VI
Round Australia	7000m	3d 9h 54m (62h flying time)	H Broadbent	Puss Moth - Gipsy Major
Port Darwin-Sydney	2500m	18hrs	H L Brook	Percival Gull - Gipsy VI
Lympne-Port Natal	5000m	2d 13h 15m	Miss J Batten	Percival Gull - Gipsy VI

Route	Distance	Time	Pilot	Aircraft
London-Lisbon	1010m	6h 5m	Senhor Carlos Bleck and Lt C Macedo	Comet - Gipsy VI R
London-Paris		59 mins	H Buckingham	Comet - Gipsy VI R
London-Paris		53 mins	Capt H S Broad	Comet - Gipsy VI R
Paris-Casa Blanca	1430m	7h 26m	M Mermos	Comet - Gipsy VI R
Portugal-Timor and return	26250m	217h flying time	Lt Humberto Cruz and Sarg Labato	Leopard Moth - Gipsy Major
Balthurst, W Africa-Port Natal, Brazil		16h 42m	Senor J I Pombo	B A Eagle - Gipsy Major
Lympne-Auckland	14224m	11d 1h 45m	Miss J Batten	Percival Gull - Gipsy VI
Lympne-Port Darwin	9000m	5d 21h 2m	Miss J Batten	Percival Gull - Gipsy VI
Cape Town-Croydon (Easterly route)	7885m	4d 16h 17m	Mrs A Mollison	Percival Gull - Gipsy VI
Cape Town-Croydon	7863m	6d 6h 57m	F/L T Rose	Miles Falcon - Gipsy VI
Lympne-Cape Town	7300m	3d 17h 37m	F/L T Rose	Miles Falcon - Gipsy VI
Gravesend-Cape Town	6400m	3d 6h 26m	Mrs A Mollison	Percival Gull - Gipsy VI
Abingdon,UK-Cape Breton Island, Canada	2612m	21h 35m	Mrs Markham	Percival Vega Gull - Gipsy VI
Portsmouth-Johannesburg	6154m	2d 4h 57m	C W A Scott and G Guthrie	Percival Vega Gull - Gipsy VI
UK-New Zealand	14000m	20 days	L Clark	Percival Gull - Gipsy Major

1937

Port Darwin-Lympne	9900m	6d 8h 25m	H F Broadbent	Leopard Moth - Gipsy Major
Cape Town-Heston	6980m	4d 18m	H L Brook	Percival Gull - Gipsy VI
Port Darwin-Lympne	9900m	5d 18h 15m	Miss J Batten	Percival Gull - Gipsy VI
Croydon-Cape Town	6870m	1d 21h 2m	F/O A E Clouston & Mrs Kirby Green	Comet - Gipsy VI R
Hatfield-Lisbon (non-stop)	1100m	5h 17m	Lt C C Macedo	Comet - Gipsy VI R

1938

London-Blenheim, New Zealand	13179m	4d 8h 20m	F/O A E Clouston and V Ricketts	Comet - Gipsy VI R
London-Sydney	11786m	3d 8h 56m	F/O A E Clouston and V Ricketts	Comet - Gipsy VI R

APPENDIX VI

Serial No. 28

DEVELOPMENT OF THE

DE HAVILLAND

'GOBLIN' JET PROPULSION ENGINES

1940 — 1945

A D D E N D U M   I.

PRINCIPAL EVENTS   1940/1945.

1940

NOVEMBER
: The Company's interest was aroused in jet propulsion engines through an official request to assist Messrs. Vauxhall Motors Ltd. in the design of an accessory box for the Whittle engine being developed by Messrs. Power Jets Ltd.

DECEMBER
: The problems associated with the development of a jet propulsion engine were discussed with Messrs. Power Jets Ltd. with special reference to the Whittle design, as practised by Power Jets.

1941

JANUARY
: The question of the Company undertaking the design and production of a jet propulsion engine was discussed between Major F.B.Halford and Sir Henry Tizard, and a visit was paid to the Gloster Aircraft Company, where airframes for the Power Jets engines were under construction.

FEBRUARY
: After discussions between the Engine and Aircraft Divisions of the Company, a rough design of the proposed de Havilland jet propulsion engine was prepared. This design was based on a single-entry impeller and straight through combustion chambers with 3000 lb. static thrust as the objective.

MARCH
: The Company carried out a general investigation into the design of a jet propulsion engine and the aircraft in which it would be installed. A visit was paid to the R.A.E., Farnborough, for discussions on aircraft design.

APRIL
: Serious design work was commenced on the de Havilland engine which differed from the Whittle design in that it had a single-entry impeller and straight through combustion chambers, whereas the Whittle engine had a double-entry impeller and reverse flow combustion chambers.

AUGUST   The first drawings for the de Havilland prototype engine were issued, and performance estimates were sent to the Ministry of Aircraft Production. The prototype engine was named the "H.1" engine.

NOVEMBER   Test rig results on a single straight through combustion chamber were sufficiently satisfactory to enable the design of the first series of combustion chambers to be finalised.

1942

JANUARY   Assembly of the prototype engine was commenced and the prototype combustion chamber underwent calibration and endurance tests on the combustion chamber test rig.

FEBRUARY   A trial assembly of the first H.1 engine was made and the prototype combustion chamber completed 150 hours running on load, including 45 hours under observed conditions.

APRIL   Motoring tests were carried out on the first H.1 on the test bed at Hatfield on Monday, 13th April, 1942, 248 days from the time when the first drawing was issued and this engine completed its half-hour acceptance test on Wednesday, 15th April, 1942. The total running time for these first tests was 80 minutes, at speeds up to 5000 R.P.M.

MAY   A demonstration run of the prototype H.1 engine was made before members of the Gas Turbine Collaboration Committee, on the 2nd May, 1942.

JUNE   The first H.1 engine attained the designed performance on the 13th June, 1942, just about nine months from the time when the first drawing was issued. The actual corrected figures obtained on this test at the full designed speed of 10,500 R.P.M. were 3010 lb. thrust, 1.233 lb/hr./lb. specific fuel consumption, and 625° jet pipe temperature. The best economy was obtained at 9500 R.P.M. where the specific fuel consumption was 1.207 lb/hr./lb. for a thrust of 2218 lb. and a jet pipe temperature of 520°C.

DECEMBER   By the end of December, 1942, three more H.1 engines had passed their acceptance tests.

1943

MARCH
The first flight, lasting six minutes, of an aircraft fitted with H.1 jet propulsion engines, took place on Friday, 5th March, 1943, within twelve months of the first test-bed trial of the prototype engine. This flight was made on the twin-engined Gloster F9/40 aircraft. The engines were rated at 2000 lb. thrust at 9000 R.P.M.

SEPTEMBER
The first flight, lasting 26 minutes, of the D.H.100 aircraft fitted with an H.1 jet propulsion engine, took place on Friday, 10th September, 1943. The engine was rated at 2300 lbs. thrust at 9500 R.P.M.

A 25 hours special category test was completed at a maximum rating of 2300 lb. thrust at 9500 R.P.M.

OCTOBER
An H.1 engine was despatched to the U.S.A. for installation in the Lockheed XP.80A aircraft. A second H.1 engine completed a 25 hours special category test at a maximum rating of 2300 lb. thrust at 9500 R.P.M., with stubless combustion chambers.

DECEMBER
A 25 hours special category test was completed at a maximum rating of 2500 lb. thrust at 9800 R.P.M.

By the end of December, 1943, a total of fourteen H.1 engines had passed their acceptance tests. Of these, two had been despatched to the U.S.A. for flight development on the Lockheed Xp.80A aircraft; two were being used for flight development on the Gloster F9/40 aircraft; one was being used for flight development on the D.H.100 aircraft, and the remainder were being used for miscellaneous development work.

During this month an agreement was completed with Allis-Chalmers, Milwaukee, U.S.A., for the manufacture of "Goblin" engines in America.

1944.

JANUARY
The first flight of the single-engined Lockheed XP.80A aircraft took place in the U.S.A. on Saturday, 8th January, 1944. Altogether five successful flights were made during the month.

The first series of flights of the second D.H.100 aircraft was made.

FEBRUARY   Successful flights were made with the D.H.100 aircraft at
42,000 ft. with no trace of surge, at a rating of 2500 lbs. and
9500 R.P.M.

A demonstration flight of the D.H.100 took place before members
of the Gas Turbine Collaboration Committee on Saturday,
5th February, 1944.

A 25 hours special category test was completed at a maximum
rating of 2700 lb. thrust at 10,000 R.P.M., and the decision was
taken to increase the rating of the engine for the Gloster
Meteor II aircraft from 2300 to 2500 lb.

MARCH   During this month a total of over 100 hours flying with true jet
propelled aircraft was completed.

The first trials of the Lucas "flower-pot" combustion chamber
were carried out.

During this month the compressor assembly from an H.1 engine
suffered irreparable damage while undergoing performance tests
on a steam turbine driven test rig at Northampton. This failure
destroyed the compressor casings, impeller, and mainshaft, and
was thought to have originated from a rub between the impeller
and the casing, and the production of magnesium dust which
collected in the rather tortuous delivery passage in the test
rig and then exploded. Rubs had occurred in actual engines
without serious consequences, but in those cases the delivery
passage was more direct. The Northampton failure occurred after
about two hours running while the compressor was operating at
the maximum speed of 10,400 R.P.M., and it should be noted that
during the previous month a total of 40 hours running had been
completed without mishap, during which it was found that the
full speed of 10,400 R.P.M. was obtained for a power absorption
of 6000 H.P.

APRIL   The D.H.100 aircraft established on endurance achievement for
jet propelled aircraft by remaining in the air for 105 minutes
and landing with sufficient fuel still in the tank to establish
its endurance for two hours. During this flight no special
precautions were taken to cruise under the most economical
conditions.

During this month, a serious failure occurred on one H.1 engine
which caused considerable damage to the compressor assembly.
The failure occurred after the first five hours of a special
category test while the engine was being run up to a maximum
speed on the test bed.

An engine was despatched to U.S.A. with a rating of 2700 lb.
static thrust at 10,000 R.P.M. for use as a flight spare for
the Lockheed XP.80A aircraft.

MAY   During this month flights were made with the D.H.100 aircraft
              at speeds in excess of 500 M.P.H. at all altitudes above
              30,000 feet. The engine was rated at 2500 lb. static thrust
              at 9800 R.P.M.

Two more failures of H.1 compressor assemblies occurred during
test bed running this month. Both failures caused considerable
damage, and both were similar to the failure which had occurred
on another engine in the preceding month. Subsequent examination of the three failures was largely centred round the
impellers and front casings, but no serious material defects were
found. Micro-examination revealed, however, a considerable
variation in the dispersion of hardening constituents in the
impeller alloy, and some micro-porosity in the front casings.
It was therefore decided to take steps to improve the material
properties of the impellers and front casings and to aim at
achieving a more uniformly distributed fine structure in the
impeller.

AUGUST   An H.1 engine completed a run of 150 hours duration starting with
              25 hours at a rating of 2700 lb. thrust at 10,000 R.P.M., and
              continuing at a rating of 2500 lb. at 9800 R.P.M.

SEPTEMBER   A fourth H.1 compressor assembly failure occurred on the test
              bed during this month. This failure was similar to the three
              previously experienced.

OCTOBER   A test of 100 hours duration under Type Test conditions was
              completed on an H.1 engine at a rating of 2700 lb. thrust at
              10,000 R.P.M. The turbine wheel assembly on this engine had
              completed more than 300 hours total running while the impeller
              running time was approaching 400 hours.

NOVEMBER   An H.1 engine completed a 25 hours special category test during
                which a maximum thrust of 2920 lb. at 10,000 R.P.M. was recorded,
                and this test was followed by a 5 hours cycle during which a
                maximum thrust of 3280 lb. at 10,250 R.P.M. was recorded.

                Another H.1 engine completed its third 100 hours cycle during
                which a maximum thrust in excess of 2800 lb. at 10,000 R.P.M. was
                attained. The major components of this engine had completed
                400 to 500 hours of high-duty running.

                During this month successful starting of an H.1 engine was
                carried out in the Lucas cold chamber at temperatures down to
                -20°C.

DECEMBER   During this month successful starts were obtained from an H.1
                engine in the Lucas cold chamber at temperatures down to -40°C.
                These tests indicated that turbine engines were inherently good
                starters, but that problems of lubrication and of electrical out-
                put from batteries at low temperatures required careful consider-
                ation.

                In the U.S.A., and H.1 engine was installed by Curtiss as an
                auxiliary engine in a Grumman airframe, and ground and flight
                tests were carried out.

                By the end of December 1944, twenty-four H.1 engines had been
                completed, and had passed their acceptance tests.

                                        1945

JANUARY   Between the 14th and 24th January, 1945, an H.1 engine (renamed
                the "Goblin" engine), completed a full Service Type Test at a
                rating of 2700 lb. static thrust at 10,000 R.P.M. This test was
                the first official approval test ever carried out on a jet pro-
                pulsion engine, and was completed in less than four years from
                the issue of the first drawing.

FEBRUARY   During this month the De Havilland Engine Company received Turbine
                Engine Technical Certificate No.1, (M.A.P. Contract No.
                S.B.27774/C.26(b)), dated 27th February, 1945. This certificate
                stated:-

"This is to certify that the DE HAVILLAND
GOBLIN 10.X/2 engine No. H.1/1020-A454519
satisfactorily completed, between 14th and
20th January, 1945, a 100 hours SERVICE
TYPE TEST to the requirements of the Ministry
of Aircraft Production turbine engine test
schedule; this being the first gas turbine
engine to pass a type test."

During the month a Goblin engine completed 100 hours
endurance running strictly in accordance with DSP
schedule at a maximum rating of 3000 lb. thrust at
10,200 R.P.M.

This month also witnessed the completion of 500 to
600 hours running of the components of a Goblin engine,
the actual running times being as follows:-

Impeller	587 hours
Front Casing	598 hours
Diffuser Casing	551 hours
Turbine Disc	518 hours
Turbine Blades	488 hours

An engine was despatched to Allis Chalmers, U.S.A., for
use as a calibrated unit.

MARCH   A Goblin engine with slight modifications to the diffuser
passages developed a corrected maximum thrust of 3300 lb.
at 10,500 R.P.M.

Development on injector-igniter equipment was successful
in enabling re-lighting to be carried out with the engine
running at 6000 R.P.M.

The first turbine rotating blade failure in flight occurred
during this month. Despite the noticeable vibration which
occurred after the loss of a portion of this blade, the
pilot succeeded in reaching his home aerodrome. The flying
time after the onset of undue vibration was 10 to 15
minutes. The blade was of Rex.78, a material which is
now obsolete for these blades.

APRIL   A 25 hours endurance run was completed on a Goblin engine
to DSP specification No.1 at 2500 lb. maximum thrust and
9800 R.P.M. with petrol as fuel.

Endurance running was in progress on a Goblin engine rated
at 3300 lb. maximum thrust at 10,500 R.P.M. Flight testing was
in Progress on D.H. "Vampire" aircraft at a rating of 3000 lb.
maximum static thrust at 10,200 R.P.M.

Goblin engines were in the U.S.A. for flight development on the
Curtiss XF-15C aircraft.

MAY   A Service Type Test was completed on a production Goblin engine
            at a rating of 2700 lbs. thrust at 10,000 R.P.M. The running was
            entirely satisfactory and the test was completed without incident.

JUNE   Completion of 25-hours Special Category Approval test, entirely
            without incident, on a Goblin engine rated at 3300 lbs. thrust at
            10,500 R.P.M.

JULY   An Official Type Test was completed on a Goblin engine rated at
            3000 lbs. thrust and 10,200 R.P.M. The performance was well
            maintained and the subsequent strip examination was extremely
            good. A noteworthy feature was that the combustion equipment was
            in use throughout the 100 hours period.

AUGUST   Successful initial flights were carried out in the U.S.A. on a
            Curtiss XF-15C navy fighter using a Goblin engine of Allis-
            Chalmers manufacture.

SEPTEMBER   A 25-hours Special Category Test was completed on a Goblin
            engine rated at 3400/3500 lbs. thrust at 10,750 R.P.M.

OCTOBER   During this month news was received that a prototype Curtiss
            XF-15C navy fighter had flown for about 50 hours with a Goblin
            engine of Allis-Chalmers manufacture, the performance being
            up to expectations.

NOVEMBER   Tests were completed on a Goblin engine in the altitude test-
            cell at B.M.W., Munich. This work was started in August, 1945,
            and altogether 72 hours testing were completed without any
            form of mechanical trouble. A preliminary analysis of the
            results indicated that they were in substantial agreement with
            estimates made from flight data, being in fact slightly better
            with respect to thrust and specific fuel consumption over the
            range of speeds normally encountered in flight.

DECEMBER   During this month successful deck landing trials were made
                on an aircraft carrier with a "Sea Vampire" aeroplane
                using a Goblin II engine. These trials represented the
                first landings of a pure jet-propelled aeroplane on the
                deck of a carrier.

                5000 hours of test-bed and flight development running
                were completed on Goblin engines up to 31st December 1945.

                                ————————

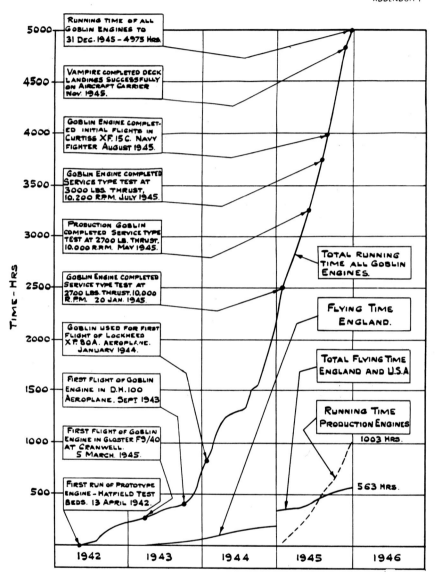

RUNNING TIME OF GOBLIN ENGINES – 1942 TO 1945.

192

APPENDIX VII

Halford Patents

Year	Patent No	Subject
1929	306591	Internal Combustion Engine
	307771	Internal Combustion Engine
1930	335568	Variable Speed Transmission Mechanism
1932/3	394777	Internal Combustion Engines
	396355	Internal Combustion Engines
	398833	Superchargers for Internal Combustion Engines
1937/8	470492	Aircraft
1939/40	503523	Transmission Mechanism
	503587	Transmission Mechanism
	503522	Transmission Mechanism
	518711	Transmission Mechanism
	504563	Ball and Socket Joints
	515621	Internal Combustion Engines
	517268	Damping Torsional Vibrations in Transmission Appartatus
1940/1	522415	Flexible Supports
	539038	Packing Rings
1941/4	544485	Transmission of Power from Internal Combustion Engines
	544486	Internal Combustion Engine Valve Actuating Mechanism
	545046	Variable Ratio Transmission Mechanism
	545047	Variable Ratio Transmission Mechanism
	545088	Engine Connecting Rods
	545128	Cooling Internal Combustion Engine Pistons
	550699	Internal Combustion Engines
	551759	Internal Combustion Engine Control
	551760	Transmitting Rotary Movements
	552154	Testing the Aerodynamic Balance of Airscrews
	552679	Mechanical Control Apparatus
	553572	Transmission Mechanism
1944/6	560606	Pieces Shaped by Grinding
	560607	Cams
	572724	Aircraft Propulsion
	573300	Aircraft Propulsion

Year	Patent No	Subject
	573496	Internal Combustion Engine Control
	574677	Radiators for Aircraft
	576032	Cooling Aircraft Engines
	578009	Turbines
	578191	Turbines
	578010	Jet Propulsion Plant
	578189	Jet Propulsion Plant
	578190	Rotary Compressors
	578765	Shaft Bearings
	578766	Controlling Temperature of Gases
	578770	Starting Turbo-Compressor Units
	579856	Turbo-Compressor Propulsive Apparatus
1946/8	580042	Turbo-Compressor Propulsive Apparatus
	591565	Turbo-Compressor Propulsive Apparatus
	591736	Turbo-Compressor Propulsive Apparatus
	591737	Jet Propulsion Apparatus
1949/50	628052	Rotary Compressors
	628342	Casting Moulds
	630792	Cooling Aircraft Turbo-machinery Bearings
	638807	Gas Turbines
1950/1	642506	Gas Turbines
	656331	Rocket-type Propulsion Apparatus
	656332	Rocket-type Propulsion Apparatus
	656333	Rocket-type Propulsion Apparatus
	656334	Rocket-type Propulsion Apparatus
	656335	Rocket-type Propulsion Apparatus
1951/2	672660	Power Plants
1952/3	680717	Rocket Motors
	680718	Rocket Motors
	695949	Gas Compressors
	697285	Centrifugal Compressors
1953/4	702455	Gas Turbine Propulsion Units
	716385	Gas Turbine Propulsion Units
	719479	Gas Turbine Propulsion Units
	719457	Rotary Compressors
1954/5	736800	Turbine and Blade Rings
	738219	Rocket Motor Combustion Chambers
1955/6	741549	Axial Flow Compressors
	741550	Axial Flow Compressors
	743357	Safety Valves

Year	Patent No	Subject
	744473	Self-Propelled Missiles
	744548	Gas Turbines
	749577	Blade Ring Assemblies
	749578	Turbine Rotor Assemblies
	757721	Liquid Fuel Engine Supply

The following Patents filed after 1955/6 were in the name of the de Havilland Engine Company coupled with the name of F B Halford.

Year	Patent No	Subject
1955/6	757230	Compressor Blade Rings
	757658	Metal Catalyst Packs
1956/7	774592	Adjustable Propulsion Nozzles
	771896	Rocket Motor Monopropellant Fuel
1958/9	808837	Blades of Turbines
	800770	Nozzle Assemblies

The following Patents were taken out in the USA.

Year	Patent No	Subject
1930	1783085	Internal Combustion Engines
1934	1977553	Mechanism for Driving Impeller of Supercharger for Internal Combustion Engines
1936	2036936	Valve Gear for Internal Combustion Engines
1940	2209884	Friction Clutch (with Napier)
	2210855	Friction Clutch (with Napier)
	2214529	4 Stroke Internal Combustion Engine (with Napier)
	2217364	Control System for Poser Units of Aircraft (with E S Moult
	2225863	Gearing for Transmitting Power (with W H Arscott)
1941	2247839	Damping Torsional Vibration in Transmission Apparatus (with Kerr Wilson)
	2239319	Flexible Supports (with C F Vickers)
	2260283	Ball and Socket Joint (with Napier & B W Harlow)

APPENDIX VIII

Royal Aeronautical Society - Halford Memorial Lectures

1959   Frank Bernard Halford 1894-1955
John L P Brodie, Engineering Director - de Havilland Engine Co Ltd

1960   Power Plants for Supersonic Transports
J S Alford, Design Eng - Large Jet, Engineering Dept - Gen Elec Co USA

1961   Aero Engines
Dr S G Hooker, Technical Director - Bristol Siddeley Engines Ltd

1962   Engine Research
R H Weir

1963   The Background of Engine Research
H Pearson, Rolls-Royce Limited

1964   A survey, chiefly historical, but with a structural flavour covering the period 1939 to 1964
R H T Harper

1965   Design and Development of Small Aircraft Gas Turbines in France
Joseph Szydlowski, Director General/Tech Director – Societe Turbomeca

1966   Engine Development and Manufacture in Sweden
G Gudmundson, Svenska Flymto AB

1967   Engine Development under the Ministry of Aviation
Peter Lloyd, Director General of Engine Research & Development, Ministry of Technology

1970   The Development of Small Gas Turbines for Aircraft Auxiliary Power
C H Paul, Director of Engineering, Ai Research Manufacturing Company of Arizona

1972 Small Engines - Big Business
J E B Perkins, Managing Director of Rolls-Royce Small Engine Division

1974 Small Gas Turbines for Helicopters
R M Lucas, Chief Engineer - Engine Projects, Rolls-Royce Small Engine Division

1976 Civil Helicopter Operations with British Airways
Operations   – Capt J A Cameron, Managing Director
Maintenance – Dr M A Parker, Deputy Chief Engineer, British Airways Helicopters

1978 Requirements and Possibilities - Rotocraft Power Plants
R R Lynn, Vice President - R&E, Bell Helicopter Textron

1982 Aero Engines – The Pursuit of yet higher fuel efficiencies
J Coplin, Director – Technology, Aero Engine Division - Rolls-Royce

1984 Helicopters
Dr J P Jones

1986 From Gipsy to Gem – with diversions
P R Stokes

1988 LHX in the Future Battlefield
R Zincone, President – Boeing Sikorski

1990 Half a century of experience in Small Gas Turbines
J R Cocheteaux

APPENDIX IX

THE HALFORD SCHOLARSHIP

THE HALFORD SCHOLARSHIP

IN order to perpetuate the name of the late Major Frank B. Halford who at the time of his death on April 16, 1955, was the Chairman and Technical Director of The de Havilland Engine Company, Limited, and who had received his education as a boy at Felsted School in Essex, it has been arranged between the Board of Directors of the Company and the Governing Body of Felsted School that an Annual Award, in the form of a Scholarship to the de Havilland Aeronautical Technical School, shall be made available to enable a Felsted scholar to receive a technical training to prepare him for a career in the aviation industry.

The scholarship will be known as The Halford Scholarship.

The Halford Scholarship will entitle a boy to receive a five-year de Havilland Engineering Apprenticeship without payment of fees and he will be paid wages in accordance with the ruling scales. In addition he will receive an annual grant of fifty pounds in each of the first two years, twenty-five pounds in each of the third and fourth years and ten pounds in the final year. In considering the monetary value of this grant, which will be reviewed from time to time in the light of current conditions, it has been decided that the amount should be adjusted in accordance with the scale of wages, which rises year by year during the apprenticeship. The amount is therefore greatest in the initial stages and lower in the final year when the boy should be practically self-supporting.

CONDITIONS OF AWARD

In March or April of each year the Headmaster of Felsted School will recommend to the de Havilland Aeronautical Technical School a suitable candidate for the scholarship for entry into the School in September. In the event of there being no suitable candidate for a September entry, the Headmaster may make a recommendation for entry at the beginning of some other term in the Technical School year.

A boy who has been recommended by the Headmaster will be asked to appear before the Selection Board of The de Havilland Aeronautical Technical School and, if accepted, it will be that Board which will award him The Halford Scholarship. It will also be necessary for the boy to pass a medical examination by the de Havilland medical officer.

The Headmaster in making his recommendation and the Board in considering the application will, in view of the late Major Halford's predominant interest in engines, give preference to a boy who wishes to serve an Engineering Apprenticeship in aero-engines rather than in other departments of the field of aeronautics.

QUALIFICATIONS

The normal academic qualification for a Scholarship shall be the Ordinary General Certificate of Education in six subjects, which must include mathematics, physics, English and one foreign language. In exceptional circumstances, however, a boy can be recommended even although he has not obtained this academic qualification if, in the opinion of the Headmaster, his attributes of capability, character and personality are such that the Headmaster considers that he would be a suitable candidate.

In all cases the Headmaster may make his recommendation in anticipation of the selected boy obtaining the necessary qualifications by the time he is due to enter the Technical School.

Except as stated above the recipient of the Halford Scholarship will be entitled to the same privileges and subject to the same rules as other Engineering Apprentices of The de Havilland Aeronautical Technical School.

ANNUAL VISITS

In order to maintain a close association between the de Havilland Engine Company and Felsted School it has been decided that a party of 20 or 30 Felsted boys be invited annually to spend a day at the de Havilland factories and establishments as guests of the Company. This visit, which is to be a permanent feature of the arrangements made to commemorate the name of Major Halford, will enable Felstedians to see something of the activities of the Engine Company and will take place, as far as is possible, in the autumn of each year.

THE AIRCRAFT INDUSTRY

In half a century the aircraft industry has risen to be one of the most important industries in the world, wielding great power in the economic and military spheres. In the 1939–45 war aircraft production became Britain's biggest industry, employing more than two million people. The advent of the gas turbine, in the course of fifteen years or so, made possible flight at supersonic speeds and, with the further development of rocket engines, far greater speeds and altitudes are being negotiated and travel beyond the Earth's atmosphere can be foreseen. Parallel with the swift progress in power units an equally remarkable advance in electronics is taking place which is not only revolutionising aerial navigation but making possible the guided missile, and, perhaps the pilotless aircraft.

The aircraft industry to-day employs scientists and engineers of the senior levels and possesses laboratories of a high order in the realms of aerodynamics, thermodynamics, electronics, metallurgy, etc. The industry offers great scope also for production engineers interested in the newest materials and methods of fabrication. It is an industry demanding not only accurate and elaborate tooling but also a large element of personal craftsmanship. It is one in which rapid technical progress is being made in many countries.

THE DE HAVILLAND ENTERPRISE

The de Havilland group of companies, representing a continuous participation since the period of the 1914–18 war, is engaged in all of the newest departments of aeronautical progress. The de Havilland Aircraft Co. Ltd. has a long tradition in civil aviation, with emphasis upon economy of operation, and has been in the forefront of high-performance military developments since 1939. It produced the first jet-propelled airliner.

The de Havilland Engine Co. Ltd., with 30 years of piston-engine experience, and for almost half of that time progressively occupied with jet propulsion, builds axial turbines for supersonic flight, also rocket engines for main and auxiliary power; the Company's laboratories are of the highest order by world standards.

de Havilland Propellers Ltd., as well as producing the full range of propellers for piston and turbine aircraft, also is engaged upon guided weapons of advanced type, involving the most up-to-date knowledge in electronics, and other fields.

The breadth of de Havilland activities, both technically and geographically, is one of the main elements in the strength of the training system that is centred upon the English companies of the Enterprise.

The de Havilland Enterprise embraces establishments in Canada and Australia, both formed before 1930, each having design and production organisations as well as considerable overhaul and servicing facilities for aircraft, engines and propellers. Both these overseas companies are entering the field of electronics and guided weapons. There are de Havilland distributing and servicing establishments in New Zealand, South Africa, and the United States of America, and the Enterprise has for many years maintained a world-wide organisation of regional managers, agents, technical and servicing staff.

THE DE HAVILLAND
AERONAUTICAL TECHNICAL SCHOOL

The de Havilland system of technical training for young men entering the industry has been in existence since the earliest days of the Company but it was in 1928 that The de Havilland Aeronautical Technical School was founded with the object of affording a comprehensive course of theoretical study in addition to the practical workshop training which had hitherto been provided.

The size and responsibility of the School have advanced with the rise of the industry, and in 1956 it has more than 2,500 young people taking courses of apprenticeship, most of them of five years' duration. The policy of the School is laid down by an Education Council which has representation from the de Havilland Aircraft, Engine and Propeller Companies and is under the chairmanship of the Chairman and Managing Director of De Havilland Holdings Ltd. The Council is assisted by Education Boards comprising senior executives representative of the main departments and factories of all three companies. The governing body was formed in 1943.

THE CHANNELS OF OPPORTUNITY

The main channels of opportunity for young men in the de Havilland Companies, and other concerns in the industry, may be broadly divided between design, production, servicing, sales and administration. For the three technical channels the de Havilland School affords a comprehensive training over a period of five years, with opportunities for courses to take specialised diplomas and degrees. In brief, the course of study is aimed at providing young men with a general and technical education fitting them for careers in aviation according to their bent. There is, therefore, every educational opportunity for an entrant to rise to the highest positions the industry holds, in this or any country and it is interesting to note that many of those who now hold senior positions in the de Havilland Companies received their early training at the Technical School.

The apprentice is trained from the outset in

either the Engine Company, the Aircraft Company or the Propeller Company. The Engine Company has apprenticeship organisations at its factories at Leavesden near Watford in Hertfordshire, and at Edgware in Middlesex. The Aircraft Company has organisations at its factories at Hatfield in Hertfordshire, at Chester, and at Christchurch and Portsmouth in Hampshire. The Propeller Company has organisations at its factories at Hatfield, and at Bolton in Lancashire. The courses of training differ as between the three companies, emphasis in the Engine and Propeller Companies being placed upon mechanical and electrical engineering.

The Halford Scholarship is primarily intended to assist Felstedians who are seeking a career in The de Havilland Engine Co. Ltd.

THE ENGINEERING APPRENTICESHIP

GENERAL

The training afforded by the de Havilland Engineering Apprenticeship, and the qualifications that can be secured upon completion, are designed to fit a man for a career leading to an executive position in the de Havilland Enterprise. The apprenticeship normally occupies five years and includes a probationary period of six months before indentures are signed. The apprentice is subject to the discipline of the School and the factory. In addition to the grant which will be paid in the case of the Halford Scholarship all apprentices are paid wages at an hourly rate. These rates vary slightly but an average figure for early in 1956 is £2 14s. 0d. a week during the first year, rising to about £7 a week in the fifth year. During the initial stages of the apprenticeship, that is for the whole of the probationary period and the first few months of the apprenticeship proper, the practical instruction, covering the use of hand and machine tools in various types of fabrication, is undertaken in the School workshops. Thereafter it is continued in the workshops and offices of the de Havilland factories, the engineering apprentice spending a period in each of the appropriate departments, beginning with those which afford ground work of the least specialised nature. The importance of training the young man in the actual factory departments where his sense of responsibility is developed from an early age is considered an important feature of the system of instruction. The progress of each apprentice is carefully watched and recorded throughout the entire course.

The theoretical classes, which are organised in conjunction with the county education authorities, commence from the probationary period and are held partly in the evenings. Some subjects of general education are included such as social studies and English.

In the previous chapter reference was made to the three main channels of opportunity for technical men in the aircraft industry—design (including development, research, etc.), production and servicing. A provisional allocation to one channel or the other, according to apparent suitability, is made at the start of the apprenticeship but, as the early training is not specialised, this matter can be kept under review during the first year or two, when particular talents will become evident.

Engineering apprentices who show ability in the more theoretical subjects such as design, stressing, aerodynamics, thermodynamics, etc., are prepared for the following examinations:

B.Sc.(Eng.). (In this case certain qualifications are required to be held before the Technical School training commences.)

Diploma in Technology (Engineering), [Dip. Tech. (Eng.)]

A.M.I.Mech.E. (by way of the Ordinary and Higher National Certificates).

A.M.I.E.E. (by way of the Ordinary and Higher National Certificates).

A.F.R.Ae.S. (by way of the Ordinary and Higher National Certificates).

A.M.I.P.E. (by way of the Ordinary and Higher National Certificates).

Those who are interested in Laboratory work may study for the examinations of the Institute of Metallurgists. Men with a bent for production engineering prepare for the Associate Membership Examination of the Institute of Production Engineers, again in conjunction with the Higher National Certificate.

Apprentices who are considered more suitable for a career on the servicing side prepare for the examinations of the Society of Licensed Aircraft Engineers and the examinations of the Ministry of Transport and Civil Aviation to qualify for Aircraft Engineers' Licences.

These examinations are taken in the fourth and fifth years of apprenticeship and the young man may then take a position or proceed to his national service. More advanced study on specialised subjects may be undertaken in the evenings or as a part-time day course, making use of technical colleges or universities. The de Havilland Companies assist and encourage promising apprentices to obtain these higher qualifications, which are indeed valuable in industry.

Although the School is primarily concerned with providing a technical training, the engineering apprenticeship provides an excellent grounding for those who have a leaning towards the business and administration sides of the industry such as the sales, accountancy and the secretarial departments. Suitability for this side is usually manifest in the later years of apprenticeship, and the training is then biased accordingly. One of the more important subjects is works and cost accountancy, and in appropriate cases this subject may be taken from an early year.

ACCOMMODATION

It is necessary for apprentices to make their own arrangements with regard to accommodation. They will be assisted in this, so far as is practicable, by the welfare sections of the School and of the de Havilland Companies to which they are attached, but unfortunately it is not possible for the School to accept responsibility for the finding of suitable accommodation.

A hostel is maintained at Hatfield to provide a temporary solution to the problem in cases of difficulty and it may be possible to accommodate a new apprentice for a short period while a more permanent living arrangement is being sought.

MESSING

Mid-day meals and other refreshments are taken at the factory canteens and are available at low prices.

MEDICAL CARE

The Medical Officer, with a trained staff, is in touch with the conditions under which all apprentices live and work. In addition the School, as distinct from the Works, has a First Aid and Welfare section and the boys are medically examined at prescribed intervals. Those from overseas or otherwise separated from their parents find this section helpful.

SPORTS AND RECREATION

Facilities are available for boys to participate in most outdoor games, and they are encouraged to take part in games which engender the team spirit. Playing fields are provided for rugby and association football, cricket, tennis, etc.

There are many clubs and societies within the organisation covering such subjects as art, photography, music and amateur dramatics. All of these are open to trainees—indeed, apprentices are keenly welcomed into their membership and activities.

LIBRARY

An excellent general library, with branches, at which almost any book can be obtained, is available on company premises, with reading rooms open to all who are under training. The engineering section covers all the technical subjects required whilst attending the School. Newspapers, periodicals and other publications are provided in the reading rooms.

CLOTHING

The practical work is hard on clothing. It is essential that every boy should possess suitable overalls.

HOLIDAYS

During the first year of training boys have a short holiday at Easter and a summer vacation of two weeks. Afterwards they take the same holidays as apply at the factories in which they are working.

BIBLIOGRAPHY

Banks, FR	I kept no diary *Airlife Publications, 1978*
Baring, Maurice	Flying Corps Headquarters 1914-1918 *Heineman, 1930*
Barker, R	The Royal Flying Corps in France – From Mons to the Somme *Constable, 1994*
Bentley, WO	WO An Autobiography *Hutchinson, 1958*
Bickers, RLT	The first Great Air War *Hodder and Staighton, 1988*
Boddy, William	The history of the Brooklands Motor Course *Grenville, 1979*
Bolster, John	Specials *G T Foulis, 1949*
Boyle, Andrew	Trenchard: man of vision *Collins, 1962*
Brodie, John LP	The development of the de Havilland series of engines for light aircraft *Proceedings of IMechE, Automobile Division, 1950-51 p48-*
Brodie, John LP	Frank Bernard Halford 1894-1955 *Journal of the Royal Aeronautical Society, April 1959, p193-205*
Bruce, JM	The aeroplanes of the Royal Flying Corps *Putnam*
Burls, GA	Aero engines – circa 1918 *Charles Griffin, 1918*
Clew, Jeff	British racing motorcycles *Haynes, 1980*
de Havilland, Geoffrey	Sky Fever – The autobiography of Sir Geoffrey de Havilland *Hamish Hamilton, 1961*
Demaus, AB Goodall, MH	Lionel Martin – a biography Flying Start – Flying Schools & Clubs at Brooklands *Brooklands Museum Trust, 1995*
Grierson, J	Jet Flight *Salmpson Low, 1945*

Gunston, Bill	World encyclopaedia of aero engines *Patrick Stephens Limited, 3rd edition 1995*
Halford, FB	Jet Propulsion *Journal of the Royal Society of Arts, 16 August 1946*
Hartley, P	Brooklands Bikes of the Twenties *Angus, 1980*
Hooker, Stanley G	Not much of an engineer *Airlife, 1984*
Hunter, I & Archer, A	Aston Martin – 1913/1947 *Osprey, 1992*
Johnson, H	Wings over Brooklands *Whittler, 1981*
Lewis, Peter	Squadron histories since 1912 RFC RNAS RAF *Putnam, 1959*
Mackersey, Ian	Jean Batten – The Garbo of the Skies *MacDonald, 1990*
Motor Sport	1926 June, July, September, November
Motor Sport	1932 December
Motor Sport	1939 February, September
Moult, Dr ES	The Whys and Wherefores of de Havilland Turbine Design *de Havilland Gazette, February 1946*
Moult, Dr ES	The Development of the Goblin Engine *RAeS lecture, 8 May 1947*
Moult, Dr ES	An Engine Designers Scrapbook *Inst Mech Engs (Automobile Div), October 1965*
Moult, Dr ES	de Havilland Engines – some recollections *Royal Aero Society, September 1978*
Nixon, F	Aircraft Engine Development during the past half century *Royal Aero Society, 1966*
Lord Kings Norton	The Beginnings of Jet Propulsion *Royal Society of Arts, September 1985*
Ricardo, Sir Harry	Memories and Machines – The Pattern of My Life *Constable, 1968*
Ricardo, Sir Harry	The Sleeve Valve Diesel Engine *Royal Society, 1950*
Royal Aeronautical Society	Frank Bernard Halford – A Tribute *The Journal, Vol 59, June 1955*
Schlaifer, Robert & Heron, SD	Development of aircraft engines and aviation fuels *Havard University, 1950*

Sharp, C Martin	DH – A history of de Havilland *Faber & Faber, 1960*
Stokes, Peter	From Gipsy to Gem – with diversions 1926-1986 *Rolls-Royce Heritage Trust, 1987*
Sturtevant, Ray	British Research & Development Aircraft – Seventy Years at the Leading Edge *Haynes, 1990*
Turnhill, R & Reed, A	Farnborough – The story of RAE *Robert Hale, 1980*
Walkerley, R	Brooklands to Goodwood – history of the British Automobile Racing Club *G T Foulis, 1961*
Whittle, Frank	Jet – The story of a pioneer *Frederick Muller Ltd, 1953*
Williams, AJ	The RFC/RAF engine repair shops – Pont de l'Arche *Cross & Cockade, 1986*
Wilson, Charles & Reader, William	Men and machines – A history of D Napier & Son Engineers Ltd 1908-1958 *Weidenfeld and Nicholson, 1958*

INDEX

Aircraft

Companies/Organisations/Establishments

Engines

Events

Illustrations (sources are credited in the captions)

R W G Hinds and Halford by wreck of 50hp Gnome Bristol Boxkite after propeller burst at 100 feet. Hinds was pilot but unhurt – Brooklands, 19 October 1913   25

Ready to race at the *White House* – September 1912   16

Renault 80 bhp vee-8 engine 1915/18 from which Cirrus 4-cylinder used many parts   74

Return of Royal Flight around Europe 23 May 1952 in the DH Comet. Halford talks with HRH The Princess Margaret and Queen Elizabeth with F T Hearle of de Havilland   130

Returning from the JCC 200 in which FBH came tenth overall   69

Short Mayo Composite – upper component 'Mercury' fitted with 4 Rapier engines   100

Siddeley Puma 6-cylinder 230bhp   41

Sir Harry Ricardo   46

The famous Blue Bird restaurant – Brooklands 1913   27

The Goblin rotating assembly seen from the impeller end   119

The team – 1930s to 1950s   111

The White House, Edwalton   17

Triumph Ricardo 500cc production road model 1922   50

W G Barlow with his 1923 short chassis GP replica Aston Martin – Halford used the chassis for his AM Special   66

Personalities

Waley Cohen Robert   47
Walker, C C   122
Winkler, Dr Johannes   131

Places

Vehicles

The Historical Series is published as a joint initiative by the Rolls-Royce Heritage Trust and The Sir Henry Royce Memorial Foundation.

Also published in the series:

No.1   Rolls-Royce – the formative years 1906-1939
        Alec Harvey-Bailey RRHT 2nd edition 1983 (out of print)

No.2   The Merlin in perspective – the combat years
        Alec Harvey-Bailey, RRHT 4th edition 1995

No.3   Rolls-Royce – the pursuit of excellence
        Alec Harvey-Bailey and Mike Evans, HRMF 1984

No.4   In the beginning – the Manchester origins of Rolls-Royce
        Mike Evans, RRHT 1984

No.5   Rolls-Royce – the Derby Bentleys
        Alec Harvey-Bailey, HRMF 1985

No.6   The early days of Rolls-Royce – and the Montagu family
        Lord Montagu of Beaulieu, RRHT 1986

No.7   Rolls-Royce – Hives, the quiet tiger
        Alec Harvey-Bailey, HRMF 1985

No.8   Rolls-Royce – Twenty to Wraith
        Alec Harvey-Bailey, HRMF 1986

No.9   Rolls-Royce and the Mustang
        David Birch, RRHT 1987

No.10   From Gipsy to Gem with diversions, 1926-1986
        Peter Stokes, RRHT 1987

No.11   Armstrong Siddeley – the Parkside story, 1896-1939
        Ray Cook, RRHT 1989

No.12   Henry Royce – mechanic
        Donald Bastow, RRHT 1989

No.14   Rolls-Royce – the sons of Martha
        Alec Harvey-Bailey, HRMF 1989

No.15   Olympus – the first forty years
        Alan Baxter, RRHT 1990

No.16   Rolls-Royce piston aero engines – a designer remembers
        A A Rubbra, RRHT 1990

No.17   Charlie Rolls – pioneer aviator
        Gordon Bruce, RRHT 1990

No.18   The Rolls-Royce Dart – pioneering turboprop
        Roy Heathcote, RRHT 1992

No.19   The Merlin 100 series – the ultimate military development
        Alec Harvey-Bailey and Dave Piggott, RRHT 1993

No.20   Rolls-Royce – Hives' turbulent barons
        Alec Harvey-Bailey, HRMF 1992

No.21   The Rolls-Royce Crecy
        Nahum, Foster-Pegg, Birch, RRHT 1994

No.22   Vikings at Waterloo – the wartime work on the Whittle jet engine by the
        Rover Company
        David S Brooks, RRHT 1997

No.23   Rolls-Royce – the first cars from Crewe
        Ken Lea, RRHT 1997

No.24   The Rolls-Royce Tyne
        L Haworth, RRHT 1998

No.25   A View of Ansty
        David E Williams, RRHT 1998

No.26   Fedden – the life of Sir Roy Fedden
        Bill Gunston OBE FRAeS, RRHT 1998

No.27   Lord Northcliffe – and the early years of Rolls-Royce
        Hugh Driver, RREC 1998

Special Sectioned drawings of piston aero engines
         L Jones, 1995

Technical Series:

No.1   Rolls-Royce and the Rateau Patents
        H Pearson, RRHT 1989

No.2   The vital spark! The development of aero engine sparking plugs
        K Gough, RRHT 1991

No.3   The performance of a supercharged aero engine
        S Hooker, H Reed and A Yarker, RRHT 1997

No.4   Flow matching of the stages of axial compressors
        Geoffrey Wilde OBE, RRHT 1999

Books are available from:
Rolls-Royce Heritage Trust, Rolls-Royce plc, Moor Lane, PO Box 31, Derby DE24 8BJ